Geologists' A

The Cas

C000218815

Edited by
J. T. Greensmith

ISBN 0-900717-98-X

The Castleton Area

CONTENTS

The Castleton Area

The Castleton Area

The Castleton Area

PREFACE

Numerous universities, colleges and schools visit Castleton for a day or weekend field excursion but, surprisingly, no comprehensive guide book to all aspects of the geology and geomorphology appears to have been published so far. The present guide sets out to summarize both geological and geomorphological features to be seen on a series of day's walks around the Castleton area.

Previous guides have been short chapters in larger works covering much of the Peak District and have tended to concentrate on the stratigraphy, thereby missing many points of interest concerned with mines, mineralization and the geomorphological history. Although an essential part of the latter, caves have often been ignored in other guides or at best mentioned very briefly. They are brought in here as an essential part of the geomorphological framework.

The Itineraries are designed to be taken on foot. Each should be taken as a day's hike, carrying packed lunch and equipped for whatever the weather may be. Some of the Itineraries can be shortened to meet transport *en route,* but it should be noted that coaches cannot be taken from Castleton village up through the Winnats Pass and the detour is a long one through Bradwell, Tideswell and Peak Forest.

The Castleton area is within the Peak District National Park and much of the land crossed by the Itineraries is in the care of the National Trust or its tenant farmers. In view of its geological, mineralogical and geomorphological interests, much of the Castleton area has been scheduled by English Nature as a Site of Special Scientific Importance (SSSI).

The Itineraries have mostly been drawn up to use public footpaths, but a few short digressions are included. Leaders of parties are advised to contact the National Trust beforehand. Individuals involved in research programmes should also consult the National Trust Regional office at Clumber Park, near Worksop, Sheffield S80 3BE.

NO HAMMERING is allowed. Much of the detail of limestone lithofacies is well seen on weathered surfaces and hammering is unnecessary. Screes provide samples of both lithofacies and fossils: collecting for research purposes should only be done with the written permission of the National Trust and other landowners.

Maps:

Castleton is on O.S. 1:50000 sheet 110 (Sheffield & Huddersfield) and on O.S. Landranger Series 1 inch: 1 mile sheet for the Peak District; Castleton is also on 1:25000 sheet for the Dark Peak and on the two 1:10000 sheets SK18SW and

The Castleton Area

SK18SE. The geology is covered on British Geological Survey 1:50000 sheet 99
(Chapel-en-le Frith) and on 1:25000 Geological Sheet SK18 & part of SK17
(Edale & Castleton, 1969) and on SK18 (Castleton, 1975).
Localities noted in the text are in National Grid square SK.

Access:
There is an almost hourly bus service to and from Sheffield. Seasonal and
irregular bus services also go to Bakewell, Buxton, Chesterfield and Edale –
enquire at the Peak Park Information Office in Castle St., Castleton, or at the
Peak Park Offices, Aldern House, Bakewell, Derbyshire. The nearest railway
stations are at Hope and Edale on the Sheffield-Chinley-Manchester Regional
Railways line. Hope and Edale stations are each about 4 km from Castleton.
Hope Station is close to the Sheffield-Castleton bus route, but access from Edale
requires a hike over the Mam Tor-Losehill ridge. A minibus service runs from
Edale over Mam Nick to Castleton on summer Sundays and Bank Holidays.
N.B. The A625 road is broken by the Mam Tor landslip: cars and mini-buses
may by-pass this by driving through the Winnats Pass or by a detour through
Edale, but buses need to take a long detour via Bradwell and Peak Forest.

The Castleton Area

INTRODUCTION

Castleton lies at the western end of the Hope Valley in North Derbyshire. It is some 25 km (16 miles) west of Sheffield and 50 km (32 miles) east of Manchester. Hope Valley is drained by the Peakshole Water, a stream which emerges from the limestone close to Peak Cavern, the largest natural cave entrance in Britain. Peakshole Water is tributary to the River Noe, which rises in the adjacent valley of Edale, and that in turn is tributary to the River Derwent, which joins the Trent near Derby. Castleton has a population of some 700 people, mostly engaged in farming, in limestone quarrying or the associated cement works, and in servicing the tourist industry, though earlier it was an important lead mining centre with a population reaching 2000 at times. The village takes its name from Peveril Castle which was started by the Normans in 1086. Its obvious defensive site was probably used in prehistoric times but archaeological excavations were cut short by the outbreak of War in 1939. Pre-Roman material was found but nothing has ever been published.

The Castleton area lies at the boundary of the White and Dark Peaks, the former to the south with its limestone plateau whilst the latter is dominated by peat-covered gritstone moorlands. The area is famous for its display of Carboniferous Limestone facies relationships and stratigraphy, for the sandstones and shales of the Millstone Grit, for its mineral deposits, particularly Blue John, for spectacular landslips and for its caves and related karstic features.

There is an abundance of geological literature on the area, but no previous guide book has concentrated solely on Castleton. Cope's Peak District guide (1958) gave a brief introduction to the stratigraphy of the Castleton area. Neves & Downie's Sheffield area guide (1967) and Simpson's Peak District Guide (1982) had only brief itineraries for the Castleton area: both tended to focus on the stratigraphy. The most comprehensive work on the geology of the area is Stevenson and Gaunts' Geological Survey Memoir for the Chapel-en-le-Frith area (1971). A succinct account of the geology by the Memoir authors is on the margin of the Geological Survey map, 1:25000 sheet SK18 (1975). The lead mining industry is covered in Ford & Rieuwerts' guide (1983). Other works are referred to in the text below and listed under Further Reading.

Highly instructive geomorphological features include the dry valleys, particularly the Winnats Pass and Cavedale, the spectacular Mam Tor landslip and, of course, the extensive cave systems.

The Castleton Area

GEOLOGY OF THE CASTLETON AREA

The Basement

The limestone massif of the Peak District lies on a pre-Carboniferous basement block known only from two boreholes, one at Eyam and the other at Woo Dale east of Buxton, and from some geophysical profiles. As none of this sparse evidence is derived from the immediate Castleton area all that can be said is that at least 300 m and possibly as much as 1600 m of limestones occur beneath Castleton and that these beds rest on a basement of Ordovician slates and/or Precambrian volcanics. Geophysical profiles suggest that the basement has been subjected to block-faulting with the blocks tilted to form half-graben structures. The details of the faulting, the half-grabens and the direction of tilting of the blocks are topics still very much in the stage of alternative interpretations and controversy.

The Carboniferous Limestone

The limestones around Castleton are of upper Dinantian (=Visean) age and are shown on the accompanying map (Figure 1). They are named the Bee Low Limestones on the British Geological Survey map (sheet 99). The standard succession is given in Table 1. The limestones were mainly deposited during the Asbian stage (D_1 in the old terminology) (336-339 m.y.). The underlying Woo Dale Limestones were deposited during the Holkerian stage (S_2) (339-342 m.y.) and outcrop around Peak Forest to the southwest of Castleton. The equivalents of the Woo Dale Beds should be present in some of the deeper parts of the cave systems, though the algal limestones of Great Rocks Dale have not yet been recognized in the caves. The Bee Low Limestones are subdivided into the Chee Tor Rock below and the Millers Dale beds above with the Lower Millers Dale lava between: this appears to be the equivalent of the Cave Dale lava, though continuity has not been proved. The limestones of the highest Dinantian stage, the Brigantian (D_2) (332-336 m.y.), were probably deposited over the whole of the Castleton area but were eroded back both in mid-Carboniferous and in later times so that their northern feather-edge lies southeast of Castleton. The Upper Millers Dale lava marks the base of the Brigantian Monsal Dale beds but both that lava and the overlying limestones are preserved only in the extreme south of the Castleton area. The younger Brigantian Eyam Limestones are not represented in the Castleton area, but the overlying Longstone Mudstones appear as isolated small outcrops of thin dark calcilutites within the village. More massive Eyam Limestones are, however, present around Bradwell some 4 km to the southeast where they display both flat reefs and reef-knolls.

The Castleton Area

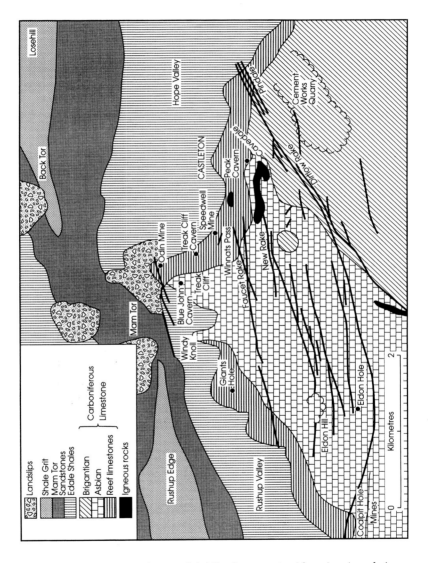

Figure 1. Geological sketch map of the Castleton area, with main mineral viens indicated.

The Castleton Area

Table 1.   **DINANTIAN STRATIGRAPHY**

Brigantian	P_2	Longstone Mudstones Eyam Limestones	
	D_2	Monsal Dale Limestones (Upper Millers Dale Lava)	
Asbian	D_1	Bee Low Limestones	Millers Dale Limestones (Lower Millers Dale Lava) Chee Tor Limestones
Holkerian	S_2	Woo Dale Limestones	

The most interesting feature of the Asbian limestones is the facies change from massif (lagoonal) to reef complex to basin facies (Figures 2 & 3). The recent incision of the Hope Valley has emphasized this facies contrast with the hills south and west of Castleton forming a marginal reef escarpment with the massif to the south and the basin largely hidden beneath the shales in the floor of the

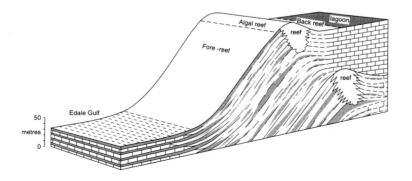

Figure 2. Diagram to illustrate the Carboniferous Limestone facies relationships across the marginal reef complex.

The Castleton Area

Figure 3. A view looking south towards the hills above Castleton village, with the fore-reef slopes rising to the massif facies of the limestone plateau to the right.

valley and the Millstone Grit hills to the north. The Namurian shales rest unconformably on the limestone and overlap the reef complex at the north end of Treak Cliff (Figure 4). The karstic valleys of the Winnats Pass (Figures 5 & 53), Cave Dale (Figure 57) and Pindale provide sections cut through the facies change from reef to lagoon. In early research it was claimed that the reef limestones were banked against an eroded cliff of massif facies (Shirley & Horsfield, 1940), but later a passage between contemporary facies was demonstrated and the cliff hypothesis was abandoned. Furthermore, the fossils showed that there was a palaeontological correlation between reef and massif facies confirming their contemporaneity (Parkinson, 1947). Much of the following differentiation into facies has been done with the aid of thin sections, but careful study of weathered rock faces shows many of the sedimentary textures.

The **massif facies**, also referred to as the lagoonal or shelf facies, is mostly crinoidal calcarenite (a coarse grained limestone) with scattered bands rich in fossil corals or in brachiopods. Sorting and roundness of clasts are variable and there is often some fine-grained matrix. Local concentrations of the fossils have

The Castleton Area

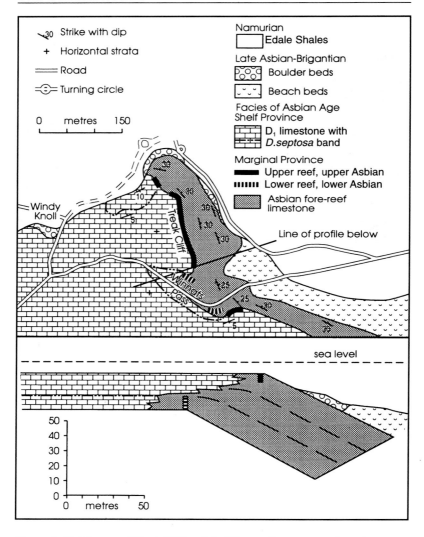

Figure 4. Sketch map of Treak Cliff and the Winnats Pass area to show the relationships of shelf and marginal reef facies (modified from Wolfenden, 1958).

The Castleton Area

Figure 5. The Winnats Pass, incised through the marginal reef complex.

been used as mapping horizons though the concentrations are really lithofacies liable to repetition or to local non-occurrence. Corals include both the solitary *Dibunophyllum bourtonense* and *Palaeosmilia murchisoni* and colonial *Lithostrotion* spp. both fasciculate and basaltiform. Though early literature refers to two *Davidsonina (Cyrtina) septosa* bands, this brachiopod is present through most of the massif sequence and only locally concentrated in distinct bands. Prominent bedding planes sometimes show pitting and other evidence of being palaeokarstic surfaces indicating brief subaerial exposure with slight erosion. Palaeosols are sometimes developed at the tops of the underlying beds.

The massif facies passes gradually into the **back-reef facies** within a few hundred metres of the reef. The back-reef limestones have more rounded clasts and a few ooliths. Many clasts are rounded but sorting is still variable, though fine-grained particles have mostly been swept away. Near the reef belt there are rather more corals scattered through the sequence and crinoid fragments tend to be larger. Brachiopods are mostly those of the massif facies, with large chonetids and productids dominant, but reef phase brachiopods are also present with *Dielasma* and *Pugnax* present. Together these fossiliferous limestones constitute a rather variable facies. In thin section there are many Foraminifera. The calcareous alga *Koninckopora* and the tubular *Girvanella* are common in the back-reef. These, and algal borings into shell fragments, suggest shallow water within photosynthetic depths.

The Castleton Area

The **reef facies** has a line of fine-grained limestone masses composed of carbonate mud; these were described as an algal reef-wall facies by Wolfenden (1958). He deduced the presence of two levels of reef-wall in the Winnats Pass and Treak Cliff area (Figure 4), and there seem to be equivalents in Cave Dale (Figure 57) and Pindale. The reef-walls mark the margin of the Derbyshire limestone massif and appear to have grown upwards rather than sideways as do many other mud-mounds elsewhere in the Carboniferous. In this they are distinct from knoll-reefs, flat-reefs or build-ups on ramps. In the fine-grained limestones weathering tends to pick out lamination, sometimes showing concentric stromatolitic masses with varying degrees of brecciation due to wave action. Having mud-grade limestones in the turbulent conditions of a reef seems incongruous but general opinion is that mats of filamentous algae grew on the surface and acted as binding agents. Rapid consolidation and lithification precluded wave erosion. Primary cavities between stromatolite heads sometimes have partial fills of internal sediment, but more often they are lined with fibrous calcite replacing filamentous algae. Thin sections reveal scattered traces of algal tubules as well as small bryozoans, sponges and tabulate corals which may have contributed to reef-building. However, recrystallization has often led to a clotted texture in the calcite mudstone with little trace of algal structures. Scattered pockets in the mudstone contain concentrations of fossil brachiopods, bivalves, gastropods, goniatites and bryozoans. The presence of algae indicates deposition at photic depths, where photosynthesis could occur.

The fore-reef, sometimes referred to as apron-reef, usually has outward depositional dips of 20° to 30°. Very variable accumulations of both fine and coarse-grained shelly detritus washed off the reef include sheets of shell limestone with abundant fossils of many types. Local unconformities and sudden changes in coarseness in the fore-reef facies may mark storm events. Small lensoid cavities with partial micrite fills and/or fibrous calcite linings are known as *Stromatactis* which was once thought to be some obscure form of fossil. Irregular bands of fibrous calcite about 1-2 cm thick in the reef and upper fore-reef are thought to be the recrystallized (neomorphic) remains of algal mats and are sometimes referred to as reef tufa.

Many of the fossil groups show a distribution controlled by their ecology across the reef belt (Figure 6). There is also some degree of bathymetric correlation of the abundance of fossil types with altitude on the fore-reef, with brachiopods and bivalves most common at the top, trilobites a little lower and crinoid debris at the bottom (Wolfenden, 1958; Broadhurst and Simpson, 1973). Up to fifty species of brachiopod, some dozen or so species of bivalves including both attached and swimming forms, gastropods, both nautiloid and goniatite cephalopods, ostracods (including giants up to 1 cm long), numerous bryozoans, scattered sponges and corals are found with scattered trilobite fragments and rare

The Castleton Area

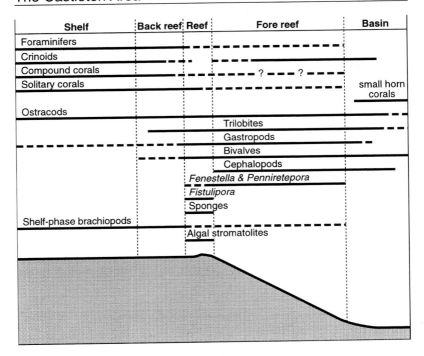

Figure 6. Diagram to show the facies distribution of various types of fossils across the reef complex (modified from Wolfenden, 1958).

fish scales. The corals include both fasciculate and basaltiform *Lithostrotion* and the small ramifying *Amplexus*. Most of the fossils show no sign of wave damage and there is little size sorting so that the conditions of deposition were sheltered perhaps largely in hollows on the outer reef slope. Lists of species are given by Parkinson (1947) and in the Chapel-en-le-Frith Memoir (Stevenson and Gaunt, 1971). The distribution of some of these fossils has been used to estimate water depths (Broadhurst and Simpson, 1973) and geopetal fabrics, produced by sedimentation within cavities, indicate that the depositional dip on Treak Cliff was around 27° and has been tectonically steepended to about 35° to the northeast. Some brachiopod species were so abundant that it was possible to collect over 1000 specimens for allometric growth studies ranging from juveniles 1 mm long upwards (Parkinson, 1954). Few of the fossils show abrasion or damage so it is likely that they were fossilized close to their life position. Lower down the fore-reef slope the limestone detritus is more fragmental and crinoid debris is predominant.

The Castleton Area

The basin facies is poorly exposed within Castleton village. It is mostly thin dark calcilutites but their relationship to the fore-reef is nowhere exposed. They may be equivalent in age to the Longstone Mudstones of latest Brigantian age, as in the Monsale Dale area some 10 km to the south. Beds apparently of this age have been penetrated in boreholes at the foot of the Winnats Pass and in Edale, but their relationship to the older Asbian fore-reef facies is not clear.

Largely on geophysical evidence a major basin is thought to extend eastwards from beneath Edale sub-parallel to the Castleton reef belt. The Edale basin appears to have a considerable thickness of argillaceous beds of Dinantian age which may have been important as a source of ions in later mineralization processes.

Volcanic Rocks

Basaltic lavas and ash layers, commonly known as toadstones, occur within the limestone sequence throughout the Peak District (Walters & Ineson, 1981). The Castleton area has two sheets of olivine basalt lava, one seen only in Cave Dale (Figure 7), and the other indifferently exposed on Cop Round above Peak Forest. Both are about 20 m thick and appear to represent the Lower and Upper Millers Dale Lavas of the Millers Dale area some 10 km to the south. At Castleton the lavas comprise multiple flows with massive basalt alternating with vesicular layers (Figure 8). Their distribution probably relates to the position of contemporary vents. The only definite vent in the immediate Castleton area is concealed beneath the floor of the Blue Circle Cement Works quarry. Another, less certainly a vent, is the patch of agglomerate near the Speedwell Mine, regarded by most geologists as material washed down from the Cave Dale lava (Figure 7). Other vents were further away, in Monks Dale near Buxton and at Calton Hill above Taddington. Occasionally, eruptions threw out clouds of fine ash which settled in the sea and resulted in the formation of "clay-wayboards": a few centimetres thick at most these provided easy ways into the rock in the days of hand quarrying. There are examples of wayboards in Cave Dale and Pindale.

The pre-Namurian Boulder Bed

From the disposition of the Brigantian limestones in the Bradwell area to the southeast of Castleton it is likely that an equivalent massif-reef-basin complex of Brigantian age once extended over the Castleton area, but it was eroded away as a result of late Brigantian uplift. This uplift saw the formation of a pre-Namurian Boulder Bed (Simpson & Broadhurst, 1969). It is present in a discontinuous outcrop around the limestone margin from Windy Knoll to the foot of the Winnats Pass. At Windy Knoll, Boulder Beds fill fissures commonly known as "Neptunean Dykes" (Figure 9). On the fore-reef slopes of Treak Cliff massive

The Castleton Area

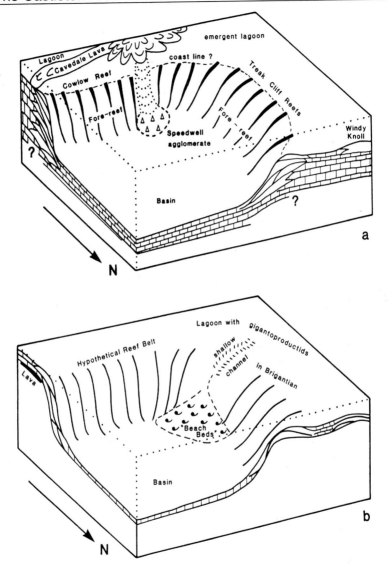

Figure 7. Block diagrams to show (a) the relationships of the Cave Dale lava to the Speedwell agglomerate, and (b) the palaeogeography at the time of the initiation of the Winnats channel and the deposition of the Beach Beds.

Figure 8. Amygdaloidal basalt from Cave Dale with the vesicles filled with calcite. The specimen is 10 cm wide.

Figure 9. A "Neptunean dyke", about 30 cm wide, filled with limestone boulders beneath the mid-Carboniferous Boulder Bed, Windy Knoll.

The Castleton Area

boulders eroded off the reef crest apparently slid down the fore-reef slope into the contemporary sea. Brigantian lagoonal limestones on the massif were also eroded and their contained fossils were washed down the slope, partly via a shallow channel on the site of the Winnats Pass to be re-deposited as the so-called Beach Beds around the foot of the Winnats Pass. The Beach Beds are thus interpreted as being at least partly equivalent to the Boulder Beds, though others have expressed the view that they are either younger or older than the Boulder Beds! The Beach Beds interdigitate with basinal muddy limestones and thin shale bands in the Treak Cliff borehole (141829) only a few hundred metres down dip. Another problem is the relationship of the Beach Beds to the Longstone Mudstones near Goosehill Hall. At present it seems that the Mudstones are younger than the Beach Beds so that it is probable that the pre-Namurian uplift was within the Brigantian. Another manifestation of pre-Namurian erosion is the solution collapse structure, later mineralized, on Dirtlow Rake, largely quarried away in recent years (Butcher & Hedges, 1987).

The Millstone Grit Series

Following the late Brigantian uplift, erosion and formation of the Boulder Bed the Castleton area was re-submerged but there was a drastic change in

Table 2. **NAMURIAN STRATIGRAPHY**

Kinderscoutian	R_1	Kinderscout Grit Grindslow Shales Shale Grit Mam Tor Sandstones
Sabdenian (Alportian) (Chokerian) Arnsbergian Pendleian	H_2 H_1 E_2 E_1	Edale Shales

palaeogeography and sedimentation, with the incoming of the deltaic Millstone Grit Series of Namurian age (Allen, 1960; Collinson, 1968), 318-332 million years ago (Table 2). The main source of the clastic sediments was remote from Castleton, being due to the rejuvenation of the Caledonian Highlands in Scotland. Rivers poured out from the Highlands and their deltaic deposits spread out southwards throughout northern England, and now form the Pennine Range of hills. At first only the distal muds reached North Derbyshire and the Edale Shales were deposited largely in anoxic conditions during Pendleian, Arnsbergian, Chokerian (=Sabdenian), Alportian into early Kinderscoutian times (E_1 to early R_1 stages). Even in these shales sedimentation was cyclic in that

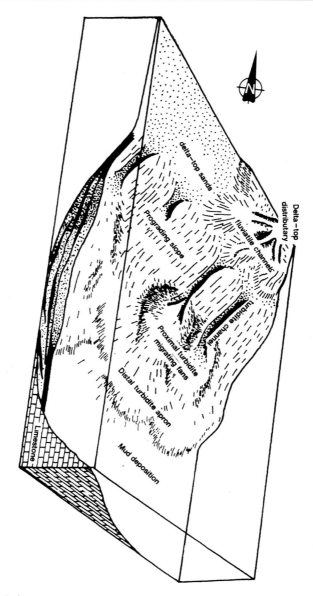

Figure 10. Palaeogeographic map of sedimentary facies during the deposition of the Millstone Grit delta.

The Castleton Area

periods of very slow deposition alternated with more rapid, giving rise to thin marine bands and thicker largely unfossiliferous shales respectively to a total of some 300 m thickness. The marine bands contain mostly pelagic goniatites and bivalves; benthonic fossils are few or absent. Diagenetic sideritic nodules are scattered throughout the shales.

During R_1 times a major sandy delta complex built out via West Yorkshire into North Derbyshire (Figure 10). This is first represented in the Castleton area by the deposition of the Mam Tor Sandstones which are about 140 m of distal fan fringe turbidites (Allen, 1960). Repeated washes of sand, silt and mud came down the delta front and were laid down as sheets of muddy sandstone around

Figure 11. Alternating sandstones and shales of the Mam Tor Sandstones at Mam Tor.

0.5 m thick alternating with similar thicknesses of silty shales (Figure 11). Each new flush of sediment-laden water scoured into the previous sedimentary sheet leaving flutes, drag marks and shale-pellet conglomerates. The flute casts, now preserved on the underside of the sandstones, suggest currents moving from north to south or NNE to SSW. The general instability of such water-laden sediments led to the formation of load casts and flame structures. The Mam Tor Sandstones thin rapidly to both the southeast and southwest and are replaced by shales within 10 km from Castleton. The distal turbidites of Mam Tor are overlain by the more proximal sandstones of the Shale Grit which is up to 180 m thick in Back Tor. In this inaptly named unit, individual sandstones commonly reach 3 m in thickness. Some show channel-fill characteristics and were deposited as lobes on the fan front. Sedimentation then changed to a greater proportion of shale laid down in the interdistributary areas of the delta. Scattered separate sand bodies are cross-sections through the channels in these beds, which constitute the Grindslow Shales (Collinson, 1968). Up to 90 m thick they herald the oncoming of the massive sheet of delta-top sandstones of the Kinderscout Grit, up to 90 m thick. These two formations are not present in the immediate Castleton area, but outcrop on the higher slopes of Kinderscout to the north of Edale. The massive sandstones are feldspathic with a few percent of feldspar at most, in contrast to the micaceous nature of the shales and turbidites. The clastic sediments in the Kinderscoutian cycle of deposition (R_1) total some 400 m in thickness. Thus a greater thickness than the whole of the Edale Shales, which represent four time zones (E_1 to early R_1), was deposited in less than one zone, a measure of the amount of coarse-grained sediment being derived from the Scottish Highlands.

The later part of the Millstone Grit Series saw several cycles of subsidence each followed by a new deltaic lobe building out. Each subsidence brought shales, with marine bands towards the base, followed by silty sands and finally a massive sheet of delta-top sandstone, commonly known in the Pennines as a gritstone. The Kinderscout Grit was followed by the Marsdenian cycle (R_2) culminating in the Chatsworth Grit, well displayed in Stanage Edge, some 8 km east of Castleton and capped by the Ringinglow Coal seam, once mined on the western limits of Sheffield. The highest Millstone Grit beds include the Rough Rock in the Yeadonian cycle (G_1). Cyclic sedimentation continued into the Westphalian Coal Measures, now represented by the Lancashire and Yorkshire coalfields, so that the limestones were buried by some 2 km of sediments by the end of the Carboniferous.

Structure

The formation of the South Pennine limestone massif was on a local high within the Pennine basin. Also within the basin there were several smaller basins: the Edale Gulf lay beneath Edale and extended ESE beneath the Derbyshire coalfield. Further away to the east were the Gainsborough and Widmerpool Troughs. The localized uplift and erosion of the limestone massif in end-Dinantian times was brought about by east-west compression which re-activated earlier fractures caused by SW-NE extensions. It created some of the fissures which later formed the mineral veins (Quirk, 1993). The basin continued to subside throughout Upper Carboniferous times, but it was "inverted" at the end of the Carboniferous, i.e. the basin became an uplifted area on the margin of a new sedimentary basin - the Permo-Triassic North Sea basin. The inversion was accompanied by NW-SE extension reactivating old faults and creating new NE-

The Castleton Area

SW faults. The complex pattern of faults provided the conduits and sites of deposition for mineralizing fluids rising from the adjacent basin (Figure 16), and so resulted in the mineral vein pattern.

Subsequent post-Carboniferous history has been of renewed uplift in Permo-Triassic times, followed by subsidence and cover by a limited thickness of Jurassic strata. Studies of hydrocarbon maturity suggest that there may also have been a substantial cover of late Cretaceous strata. Renewed uplift in mid-Tertiary times resulted in the stripping back of the Mesozoic cover.

Figure 12. Near-horizontal slickensides in Dirtlow Rake, demonstrating wrench-faulting.

Each of these structural changes affected the whole Peak District and Castleton's geology provides a sample of the story. The limestones of the massif and reef show a regional dip of around 8° to the east, reflected in the slope of the ground along Dirtlow Rake and above Cave Dale towards Bradwell. The fore-reef limestones of Treak Cliff are some 8° steeper than the sedimentary dip at the time of deposition. The Millstone Grit strata of Mam Tor and Losehill are similarly inclined to the east but at a lower angle. Westwards, however, Rushup Edge has nearly horizontal strata and lies on the axis of the Pennine anticline. The beds on its western flank dip sharply westwards towards the Lancashire Coalfield. To the north, Edale is a broad E-W anticline, with the sandstones of the Kinderscout plateau beyond lying almost horizontally.

The Castleton Area

Faulting is largely confined to the wrench faults of the major mineral veins such as Dirtlow Rake, where the walls show nearly horizontal slickensides (Figure 12). Oblique dextral shift in dipping beds has brought in higher Brigantian beds on the south side. The scrin veins of Pindale probably represent a Reidel shear pattern i.e. small curved shears developed along wrench faults (Figure 61). There was probably similar movement on New and Faucet Rakes though it is difficult to prove. The old mine plans of Odin Mine show it to have developed along a set of sub-parallel shears *en-echelon* (Figure 23). At least one fault crosses the Losehill ridge near Hollins Cross and may merge with some part of the Odin shears at depth. It is tempting to think of the reef-belt as lying across a major basement fault analogous with the Craven Faults in Yorkshire, but no such structure has been determined as yet.

Mineral deposits and mines

Largely as a result of the inversion tectonics at the end of the Carboniferous, mineralizing fluids were introduced into the limestone massif and yielded the mineral vein system shown on Figures 13 & 14. The veins have been exploited since Roman times for lead ore, but in the last two centuries they have been mined mainly for fluorspar, baryte and a little zinc ore. The veins have traditionally been classified into four categories: rakes are major fault fractures filled with hydrothermal minerals; scrins are minor fractures similarly filled; flats are deposits generally lying along the bedding; and pipes are fillings of ancient cavity systems, notably palaeokarsts (Figure 15). A worked-out rake is shown in Figure 22. A fifth category is one of replacement, where the minerals replaced the limestone metasomatically (molecule for molecule). To these may be added a further category of mineralization of a solution collapse structure, as on Dirtlow Rake (Butcher & Hedges, 1987).

The mineral suite is dominated by galena (PbS), fluorite or fluorspar (CaF_2), baryte ($BaSO_4$) and calcite ($CaCO_3$). Nearly a hundred other minerals are known in trace quantities (Ford, Sarjeant & Smith, 1993). The main minerals also occur in several varieties: fluorite (=the pure mineral) is usually colourless, but may occur opaque white, yellow, reddish or blue to purple. The banded blue/purple and white variety of fluorite known as Blue John is unique to the mines and caverns of Treak Cliff. It has been mined there since the mid-18th century for ornamental uses. Commercial fluorspar (less pure than the mineral fluorite) is still mined opencast along parts of Dirtlow Rake and its branches. Baryte is usually a cream-coloured granular variety known locally as caulk, but white crystal bladed varieties occur around Dirtlow Rake. Calcite is usually opaque white but sometimes is transparent and colourless.

The Castleton Area

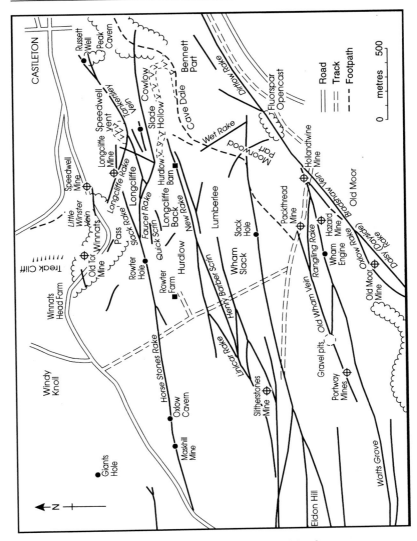

Figure 13. Sketch map of the mineral veins southwest of Castleton.

The Castleton Area

Figure 14. Aerial view, looking southwest, of mineral veins south of the Winnats Pass: New Rake on the left; Faucet Rake in right centre; Slack Rake and the margin of the Winnats Pass on right (photo by A. Pacitto).

The Castleton Area

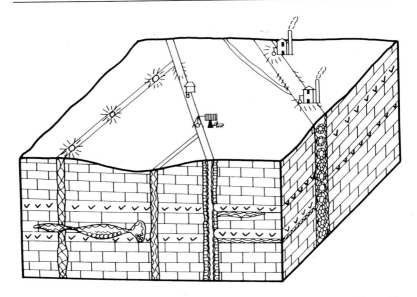

Figure 15. Block diagram to show the relationship of two rakes, scrins branching from them, flats beneath lavas, (side and front face), and a pipe vein in an ancient cavern (front face).

The process by which the minerals were deposited is complex and the many lines of evidence have been discussed by Ixer & Vaughan (1993), Quirk (1993) and Ford & Quirk (1995). In brief, the origin of the mineral veins is by the expulsion of mineralizing fluids from adjacent basins into the high provided by the limestone massif (Figure 16). The fluids pick up the ions of Pb, Zn, F, Ba from the clay minerals and other alteration products in the mud-rocks of the adjacent basins and transfer these by up-dip lateral movement into the high where they meet cooler, sulphur-bearing, more oxygenated meteoric waters and react to precipitate the mineral suite. Chronological constraints require that the basin inversion was in progress, but that the cover of 2 km or so of Upper Carboniferous bed was still mostly in place, indicating that the main episode of mineralization must have been very late Carboniferous to early Permian. The fluids have a high brine content with traces of hydrocarbons and these act as catalysts in transporting the ions to the scene of precipitation. Minute quantities of fluids trapped as inclusions in fluorite crystals show salt contents as much as ten times that of sea-water and indicate temperatures of crystallization from around 70°C to 150°C, appropriate for burial beneath 1.5 km of Upper Carboniferous sediments (though perhaps needing a correction factor of +20°C for burial beneath 2.5 km).

The Castleton Area

Quartz is rare in Derbyshire's mineral veins, in contrast to the North Pennines, but an unusual concentration occurs in the Pindale quartz rock (Orme, 1974). An area around the top of Pindale between Dirtlow Rake and the Cement Works quarry has Brigantian limestones largely replaced by this unusual type of quartzite. Under the microscope it is a mesh of needle-like quartz crystals with

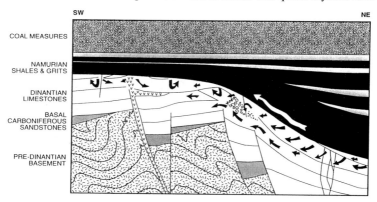

Figure 16. Diagram to show the movement of mineralizing fluids up-dip into the limestone massif (from Ford & Quirk, 1995).

small amounts of dark blue fluorite and white baryte in the interspaces. The quartz rock has weathered out and numerous residual blocks lie in the fields (Figure 17). There is a small outcrop of the quartz rock with veinlets of blue

Figure 17. Pindale quartz rock, near Dirtlow Rake.

The Castleton Area

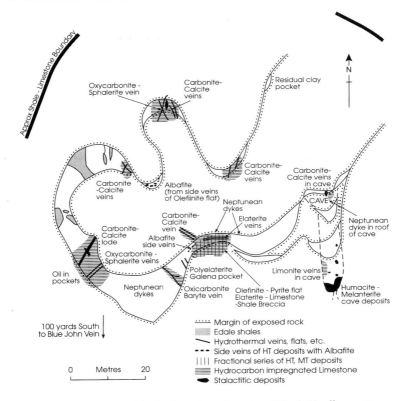

Figure 18. Sketch map of the hydrocarbon deposits of Windy Knoll quarry (modified from an unpublished diagram by G. Mueller).

fluorite forming one wall of Dirtlow Rake at one point, though the Rake itself did not contain quartz. Isolated blocks of quartz rock also occur in upper Cave Dale and west of Hazard Mine. The silica is thought to have been derived from the much altered basaltic agglomerates of the concealed volcanic vent beneath the Cement Works quarry, perhaps during an early phase of the mineralizing process.

A unique mineral assemblage of bitumens occurs in Windy Knoll quarry (Figures 18 & 19). Some thirty varieties of hydrocarbons have been recorded, including paraffinite, olefinite, albafite, carbonite and mutabilite (See Ford *et al*, 1993 for a full list). They are not minerals in the strict sense as they do not form crystals and do not have a fixed chemical formula. They are variously thought to

Figure 19. The hydrocarbon deposits of Windy Knoll inpregnating the scree facies of the pre-Namurian Boulder Bed.

be the residue of a former oil reservoir or to be lighter hydrocarbons which have been polymerized by the passage of mineralizing fluids (Figure 20). Some of the hydrocarbons have been partly oxidized, and others have suffered bacterial alteration. Various sulphides and gangue minerals are totally enclosed in bitumen and there is little doubt that the hydrocarbons played some part in the mineralizing process. They are various impregnations within the topmost beds of limestone or hosted within the pre-Namurian Boulder Bed and associated palaeo-screes at Windy Knoll (Figure 19). Elsewhere around Castleton, small quantities of bitumen are widely present as blebs within hollow fossils and other cavities in the limestone.

Whilst lead-mining started in Roman times most of the visible workings date from the 18th and 19th centuries (Ford & Rieuwerts, 1983). Lines of shaft

The Castleton Area

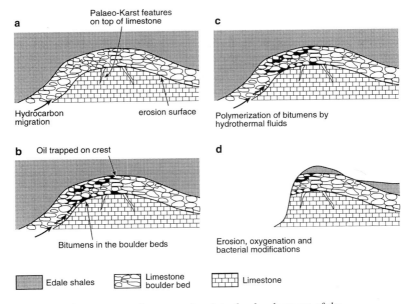

Figure 20. *The sequence of events, a,b,c,d, in the development of the hydrocarbons of Windy Knoll (modified after a diagram by K. Pering).*

hollows and waste heaps mark the courses of the veins (Figures 14 & 55). Many of the mines were single family enterprises and lasted only a few years reaching depths of little more than 20 or 30 metres. Few of these are accessible today and the best examples are on the north side of Pindale. Larger mines on the rakes were worked over several centuries. Odin Mine is known to have been worked as early as the 13th century and may date back to Roman times (Ford & Rieuwerts, 1964) (Figure 21). Many of the 18th-19th century workings on Dirtlow Rake have been obliterated by recent large scale excavations for fluorspar, but sections of open-cut near its eastern end still show pick marks from before the days of explosives (Figure 22). Workings on New Rake and its branches in the late 18th century penetrated the stream cave system of Speedwell Cavern and part of this provides the tourist underground boat trip today.

The Blue John variety of fluorspar was deposited in the voids between boulders in the Boulder Bed and in ancient cave systems in Treak Cliff (Ford, 1992) (Figures 23 & 49). There are also small-scale replacement deposits. Some fourteen varieties or "veins" of Blue John are restricted to limited parts of the cliff and may reflect vagaries of the plumbing system with attendant differences

Figure 21. A worked-out vein in Odin Mine, with waste rock stacked on stone stemples overhead (photo by Alan Coase).

Figure 22. An open-cut section of Dirtlow Rake. The walls show pick-marks from pre-explosive days.

The Castleton Area

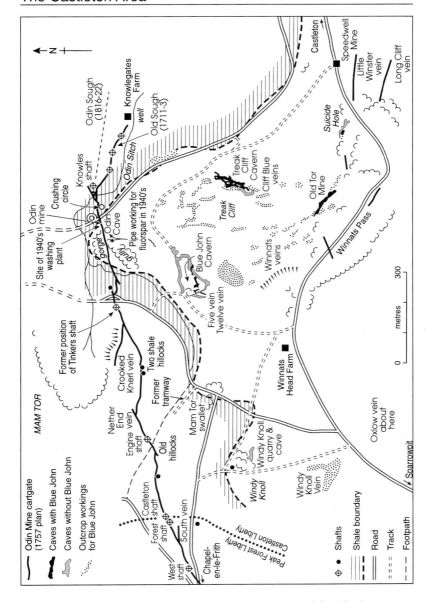

Figure 23. Sketch map of the Blue John fluorspar deposits, Odin Mine's cartgate has been taken from mid-18th century plans.

in temperature and flow. The Blue John deposits are almost mono-mineralic and only occasionally are galena, baryte and calcite associated. Parts of the Blue John deposits can be seen in the tourist Blue John and Treak Cliff caverns and in scattered surface occurrences on Treak Cliff (Figure 23). Blue John has been used for ornamental purposes since the mid-18th century and many stately homes in throughout Britain have fine examples. Chatsworth House, Kedleston Hall and the Buxton, Derby and Sheffield Museums should be visited to see their Blue John. It is still mined in small quantities and ornaments and jewellery are available in the tourist shops.

GEOMORPHOLOGY OF THE CASTLETON AREA

Introduction

Castleton lies at the western end of the Hope Valley at about 180 m O.D. It is partly surrounded by hills rising to over 500 m O.D. on the north, west and south, whilst the broad flat-floored valley extends eastwards. As the valley was eroded it exposed the northern margins of the limestone massif from beneath the Millstone Grit cover.

The stripping back of the Millstone Grit cover appears to have occurred in several phases. Part of the stripping was in Permo-Triassic times and removed the Coal Measures and some of the Millstone Grit cover from the crest of the Pennine anticline. Renewed stripping took place following uplift in mid-Tertiary times so that the general form of the limestone plateau flanked by Millstone Grit country had been established by the onset of the Pleistocene glaciations. The last provided a series of erosional phases, with the intermittent incision of Hope Valley lowering the water-table to reveal the cave systems.

Thus, most of the obvious geomorphological features evolved during the Pleistocene. These include the exhumed reef complexes resulting from the incision of Hope Valley, a loess sheet (Figure 24), dry valleys (Figure 27), solifluction deposits, screes, landslips (Figure 28) and the cave systems (Ford, 1977; Ford & Gunn, 1992).

Glaciation

The glacial history of the immediate Castleton area is full of uncertainties as there is little evidence of till or of interglacial deposits. Castleton lay in a shadow zone protected by Kinderscout so that ice streamed down both the west and east sides of the Pennines. Any ice accumulating over Castleton probably remained more or less stagnant. A few erratics of Lake District origin have been found in till probably of pre-Devensian age about 5 km to the west around Chapel-en-le-

The Castleton Area

Figure 24. Loess exposed in a mineral working below the dark soil layer (the material above the soil is mineral waste).

Frith. However, some 10 km to the south around Stoney Middleton a till sheet suggests that moving ice by-passed the Castleton area and crossed the Peak District along the general line of the Wye Valley in the Wolstonian glaciation. It is likely that at least two glacial advances affected the South Pennines, with the early phase in the Anglian stage, and some hints of these can be recognized in the morphological history of the cave systems (Ford, 1986) (Table 3, p.39). Cave sediments exposed recently in Eldon Hill quarry hint that there may have been an even earlier glaciation in pre-Anglian times.

Periglacial activity - loess and solifluction

As with glaciation there is little evidence of periglacial activity other than loess and solifluction deposits. On the limestone plateau the turf lies on a thin soil covering a metre or so of ochreous silty clay (Figure 24). Microscopic study has shown that this is finely dispersed quartz with some mica and feldspar. The quartz grains show surface textures characteristic of wind-blown transport, presumably from the adjacent Millstone Grit country (Pigott, 1962). The loessic clay has suffered some bioturbation with resultant admixture of insoluble residues from the limestone. It forms a blanket on the interfluves but there is little sign of it in the dry valleys such as Cave Dale and Conies Dale, suggesting that these may be younger features. Castleton's caves are well known amongst

cavers for their sticky mud and much of this seems to be loess washed down
fissures into the older cave passages. West of Hazard Mine shallow channels
were incised into the loess blanket by streams which once drained into caves
along a mineral vein.

There are few solifluction deposits on the limestone country but the lower
Millstone Grit slopes of Edale and Losehill are mantled with a sheet of
fragmented sandstone and shale up to about 3 m thick. It is probably best seen in
the banks of the River Noe and its tributaries in Edale. A comparable sheet
mantles the southern slopes of Rushup Edge down to the limestone boundary
and the streams have incised channels in their courses down to the swallets
(Figure 25). Although very similar to till, the solifluction sheets are thought to
have originated by the process of sludging of partly frozen ground as it thawed
out. Some solifluction material has sludged into caves, notably the upper
passages of Giants Hole, some of which are filled with a sandy gravel.

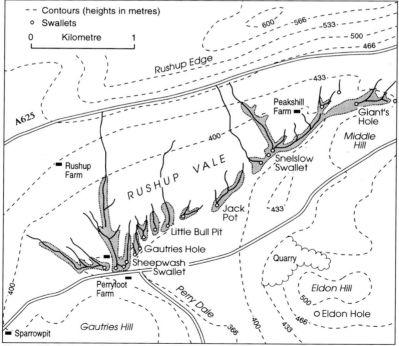

*Figure 25. Streams draining into swallets along the limestone/shale boundary
are incised into the solifluction sheet mantling Rushup Valley
(modified from a diagram by R.H. Johnson). Incised channels shaded.*

The Castleton Area

Dry Valleys

The whole of the Peak District has a network of dry valleys (Figure 26). Some, such as Peak Perry, are tributaries to one of the few active river valleys such as the Wye Valley. West of Castleton Conies Dale is a short steep dry valley

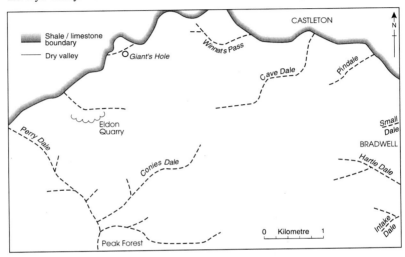

Figure 26. Sketch map of the dry valleys near Castleton.

tributary to Peak Dale. Cave Dale is a classic dry valley (Figure 27) with a short steep break in its thalweg apparently caused by the outcrop of the Cave Dale lava. Together with Pindale and the Winnats Pass with its complex history (Ford, 1987) the dry valleys immediately around Castleton grade into the head of Hope Valley. Others drain into Perry Dale and thus into the Wye drainage. All have had a phase of incision when run-off was on frozen ground; thus they are probably largely post-Wolstonian glaciation features. The Winnats Pass is anomalous in that it has so little catchment area for the highly erosive stream which must have flowed through it once. But it could have had a much more effective catchment if a tongue of ice occupied the Rushup Valley in late Wolstonian times and provided melt-water in the vicinity of Windy Knoll. The partly shale-filled proto-Winnats valley would be easily scoured out and deepened by the run-off.

No evidence has been found to support the old idea that the Winnats Pass originated by the collapse of a major cave system.

Figure 27. The upper part of Cave Dale – a classic dry valley.

Hope Valley

The wide western head of Hope Valley has a superficial resemblance to a corrie at the head of a glacial trough, but the southern and western slopes are due to the exhumation of the fore-reef limestone slopes, whilst the northwestern limit of the valley is due to the Mam Tor landslip. Misfit streams now drain the Millstone Grit slopes and join the resurging cave drainage near Peak Cavern to form Peakshole Water, the main tributary of the River Noe at Hope. This in turn joins the River Derwent some 6 km east of Castleton. Much further downstream there is a late Pleistocene terrace sequence, but this terminates in knick points at Matlock and near Grindleford so that the Hope Valley floor correlates with an Ipswichian terrace further downstream. Earlier, before Peakshole Water and its tributaries had incised to c.200 m O.D., the valley floor must have been much higher, but the limestone drainage still resurged at Peak Cavern, probably by the gorge being in effect a vauclusian spring with the water rising from considerable depth. Thus, Hope Valley itself has had a complex history of incision probably starting before Hoxnian times and being progressively incised at intervals since then.

The Castleton Area

Screes

Frost action on exposed limestone cliffs has yielded large quantities of angular limestone clasts a few centimetres across. During cold periods these mantled the lower slopes but in more recent times they have often become covered with grass and soil. In some cases water seeping from the limestones has deposited enough calcite in the scree to result in calcrete, cemented scree. Examples occur on Long Cliff, near the Speedwell Cavern, and adjacent to the Siggate road eastwards out of Castleton. Some of the screes were quarried for road-building before the days of tarmacadam.

Landslips

Perhaps the best known feature of the hills around Castleton is the Mam Tor landslip, though this is just one of a series of slips along the Rushup Edge-Mam Tor-Losehill ridge (Figures 28 & 65). At all these the turbiditic Mam Tor Sandstones have slipped downhill across the Edale Shales. On pollen and ^{14}C evidence the Mam Tor landslide is at least 3600 years old. The cause of the initial slippage is thought to be the pore-pressures of the groundwater near the sandstone/shale surface exceeding stability factors. A fault crosses the foot of the face downthrowing the base of the sandstones by some 10-20 m on the northwest side causing some damming-up of groundwater. Weathering of pyrite in the shales may have been an extra weakening factor in producing sulphuric acid which dissolved carbonate in the shales. The building of a turnpike road across the landslip in 1810, following an earlier miners' cart track, was unwise as it was followed by development as a major cross-Pennine route in the 1930s. The A625 road was in a bad state of repair by the end of World War II. It was re-aligned and curves eliminated in the late 1940s. Major repairs were again necessary in 1965 and raised questions about the effects of the vibrations caused by heavy traffic. In 1975-76 two dry summers followed by a wet winter led to increased movement and fault scarps appeared across the road in late 1976 (Figure 29). Repeated filling and levelling failed to cure the problem and the road was finally closed to traffic in January 1979 (Skempton, 1989; Doornkamp, 1990) (Figures 29 & 65). Movement has continued to the present day though at a lower pace and the remains of the road are an object lesson about the folly of building roads across unstable ground.

The form of the Mam Tor landslip is partly block rotation, partly debris flow and partly mud-flow down into the head of Hope Valley (Figure 30). The sandstones are sufficiently porous for groundwater water to lubricate movement at the sandstone/shale contact. The collapsed and slipped material flowed downwards and spread for several hundred metres onto the valley floor giving uneven boggy bracken-covered ground. The shear plane has been identified in boreholes at

The Castleton Area

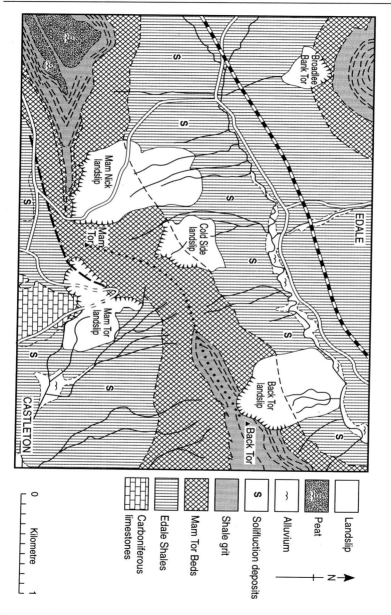

Figure 28. Sketch map of the landslips near Castleton.

37

The Castleton Area

Figure 29. Landslip disturbance of the former A625 road on Mam Tor.

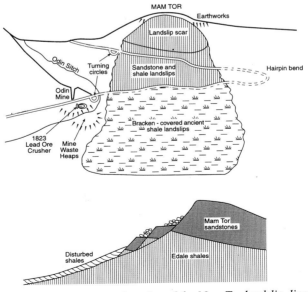

Figure 30. Diagrammatic view and section of the Mam Tor landslip, line of former A625 indicated.

The Castleton Area

depths up to 30 m below present ground surface. The Mam Tor landslip scar cuts across the ends of the ramparts of a hill fort ^{14}C dated at 1180 B.C., once thought to be an Early Iron Age date but now regarded as late Bronze Age. Rain and frost affect the sandstone face so that blocks often fall and accumulate as scree slopes at the foot of the face, only to have secondary slips develop in this fallen debris. A small older slip is present in the field northeast of the Hairpin Bend.

No evidence has been found to suggest that the proximity of the lead mine workings of Odin Mine or the shale/limestone interface are in any way involved in causing the landslide.

Other landslides are on the north side of Rushup Edge near Mam Nick, at Cold Side on the north side of Mam Tor and at Back Tor on Losehill. The last two are inactive but the Mam Nick slide is crossed by a road which shows some signs of movement damage, though it has never carried the heavy traffic of Mam Tor. The Mam Nick slide has been dated at 8000 years B.P.

Caves

With four tourist caves Castleton is famous for its underworld. The four show caves are different in character but they all form part of a long and complex history of speleogenesis (Ford, 1977, 1986) (Table 3). The development of the cave systems can be visualized as starting with the stripping back of the impervious Edale Shales off the limestone massif progressively allowing karstic drainage to exploit different weaknesses in the limestone as sites of cave inception. As the mineral rakes became exposed water could sink in one place and rise in another, usually along the same vein forming a sort of U-tube. Solution could take place enlarging the U-tubes and leading to the formation of vein-cavities, such as the Bottomless Pit Cavern in Speedwell Cavern. Some twenty such cavities are now known and the necessary phreatic drainage only required two areas of the limestone to be denuded of Edale Shales, at different altitudes, for solution to begin using fractures in the vein system. Pipe veins could also be pirated by karstic drainage. As further stripping of the Edale Shales took place water could sink along bedding and joint systems to feed into the still submerged vein cavities, thus yielding an integrated network at various levels within the limestone massif. Early stages required slow percolation along bedding planes, often marked by a thin pyritous shale or volcanic tuff horizon. The inception process by such seepage was probably very slow but once there was an hydraulic boost created by flow from sink through bedding to veins, with resurgence at a lower level, then speleogenetic enlargement could take place. Tubular phreatic passages conducted streams through the limestone massif. The main phases of cave development came when the water-table was lowered by the progressive incision of Hope Valley. Whilst Rushup Valley floor was at a much

The Castleton Area

Table 3. **Suggested Chronology of Cave Development Stages at Castleton**
(modified after Ford *et al.*1983)

Probable Stage	Process	Cave Features
Pliocene or Early Pleistocene (1-2 m.y. ago)	Phreatic solution	Development of vein cavities & high-level tubes
Early Pleistocene	Vadose trenching	Eldon quarry tubes
Early Pleistocene	Periglacial (?) fill	Eldon quarry tubes
Cromerian (>350,000 years)	Vadose trenching	High level canyons (White River Series?)
Anglian (glaciation)	Stillstand	
Hoxnian (225,000 - 170,000 years)	Vadose trenching	Incision to 218 m in main cave systems; Treak Cliff Cavern incised. Peak gorge initiated. Stalactites in Winnats Head Cave
Wolstonian (glacial)	Stillstand - glaciation	loess washed into caves
Ipswichian (145,000 - 90,000 years)	Vadose incision	Blue John Cavern incised as limestone is bared. Incision of Valley to 200 m O.D. Russet Well active.
Devensian I (periglacial)	Sediment fills	Treak Cliff Cavern stalagmites on loess
Interstadial	Stalagmite growth	Stals. in Peak Cavern, Speedwell, Giants Hole
Devensian II (periglacial)	Sediment fills	Inwashed loess
Holocene (<14,000 years)	Vadose trenching through fills	Much stal. deposition. Partial removal of sediment fills.

higher level than at present streams drained across the limestone/shale boundary to sink near Eldon Hill quarry, where ancient (at least 700,000 years old) passages have been intersected completely infilled by sediments derived from the Millstone Grit country of Rushup Edge. These ancient swallet systems were superceded by the present-day line of sinks such as Giants Hole (Figure 41 & 43). Drainage passed through the limestone massif to resurge at Castleton, thus passing beneath the apparent surface watershed. Whilst Hope Valley floor was at a much higher level than at present, water rose from the drainage system at a massive vauclusian spring where Peak Cavern gorge now lies. As the Hope Valley floor was lowered water-levels fell within the limestone and streams ran along the floors of old phreatic tubes. With the feed of abrasive sand via the swallets these streams cut canyon-like vadose slots into the floors of the old tubes. The inner passages of Giants Hole, Speedwell Cavern and Peak Cavern provide good examples. As the present swallet to resurgence systems became established some early passages were abandoned by their streams and received only percolation water, which deposited speleothems stalactites and stalagmites, as in Treak Cliff Cavern. Sometimes such speleothems rest on washed-in loessic silts demonstrating that the loess is older than the stalagmites.

The sequence of events displayed in the caverns, together with uranium/thorium dating of speleothems, enables at least a partial chronology to be deduced in relation to surface events, such as glaciations, loess deposition, solifluction and river incisions, as shown in Table 3 (Ford, Gascoyne & Beck, 1983; Ford, 1986).

Peak Cavern's vast entrance is a resurgence cave abandoned except in times of high flood conditions (Figure 31). Terraces used by rope-makers have been cut into old screes which might repay an archaelogical dig one day. Beyond the Vestibule the low Lumbago Walk is a recently drained phreatic tube, still subject to occasional flooding. The Great Cave is largely solutional along master joints, whilst the caves beyond are a recently drained phreatic system (Figures 32, 33 & 60) with a little vadose modification. Beyond the tourist route the main streamway includes a magnificent vadose canyon more than a kilometre long and 20 m high in places (Figure 34). Tributary passages are partly choked with derived loessic clay, but there is a high level system with fine stalactite and stalagmite decorations, the White River Series, accessible only to expert cavers.

Speedwell Cavern is partly an experiment in lead mining where a tunnel was carefully designed and excavated in 1771-1778 to intersect the stream caves to provide barge transport along an underground canal for both ore and waste (Ford, 1990) (Figure 35). Today's visitors still travel by boat along the Main Canal (Figure 36) to reach the Bottomless Pit solution cavern. More than 50 m high it is one of the vein cavities dissolved at an early stage of speleogenesis. Beyond the tourist route the Far Canal reaches the stream caves at The

The Castleton Area

Figure 31. The vast entrance to Peak Cavern; with remains of the rope works in the foreground (photo by Paul Deakin).

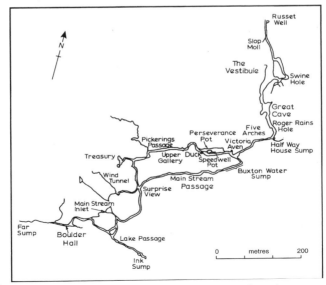

Figure 32. Sketch plan of Peak Cavern; the tourist route from the entrance at The Vestibule ends near the Halfway House.

Figure 33. Peak Cavern's phreatic tube upstream from Buxton Water Sump (photo by J.R.Wooldridge).

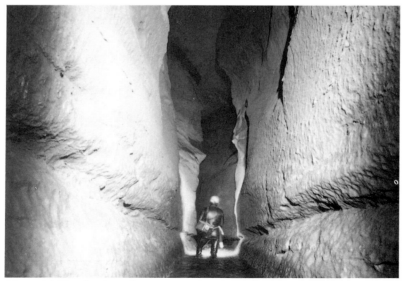

Figure 34. The classic vadose canyon of Peak Cavern's Main Streamway (photo by Paul Deakin).

The Castleton Area

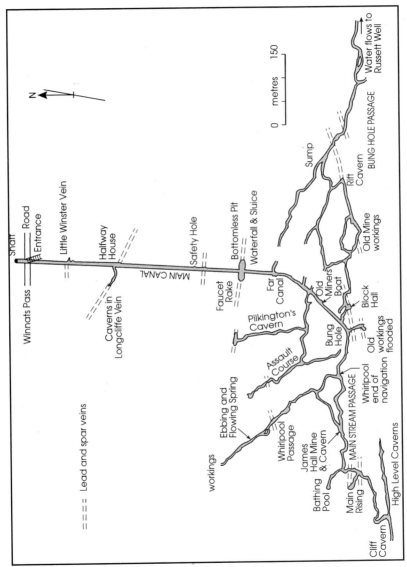

Figure 35. Sketch plan of Speedwell Mine and Cavern; the tourist route takes in the Main Canal to the Bottomless Pit.

Figure 36. Speedwell Cavern's Main Canal, excavated 1771-78.

Figure 37. The Main Rising at the upstream end of Speedwell Cavern's streamway.
This has been dived to a depth of 70m (photo by Paul Deakin).

The Castleton Area

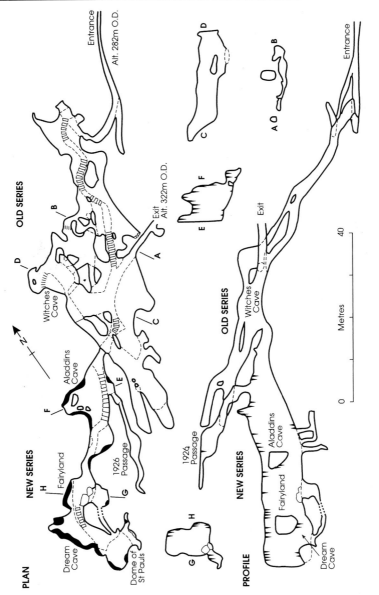

Figure 38. Sketch plan and profiles (A-B, etc. and below) of Treak Cliff Cavern: the tourist route takes in almost the whole system.

The Castleton Area

Figure 39. The profusion of stalactites in Treak Cliff Cavern's Dream Cave. The stalagmites grew on top of inwashed loessic clay.

Whirlpool, which requires swimming. The stream flows from west to east along a vadose canyon up to 10 m high. The stream rises from a flooded vein cavity at Main Rising (Figure 37). The water comes from all the swallet caves (Figure 43). Two tributary passages link with cave systems by which 18th century miners entered the system. The high level White River Series of Peak Cavern passes across the Speedwell stream caves.

Treak Cliff Cavern starts with a low tunnel through an outlier of Edale Shales on the fore-reef face of Treak Cliff (Ford, 1992) (Figures 38 & 49). The route continues uphill through the pre-Namurian Boulder Bed where many of the voids are filled or lined with Blue John fluorspar (Ford, 1969). Worked since the mid-18th century the Blue John deposits are also in palaeokarstic mid-Carboniferous caves. The inner series of caves are a short, but high and wide, vadose canyon decorated with thousands of stalactites and stalagmites (Figure 39). Its former stream was probably derived via a swallet high on the face of Treak Cliff. Derived loess underlies stalagmites which were dated at 110,000 years old (Ipswichian) by the U/Th disequilibrium method.

The Castleton Area

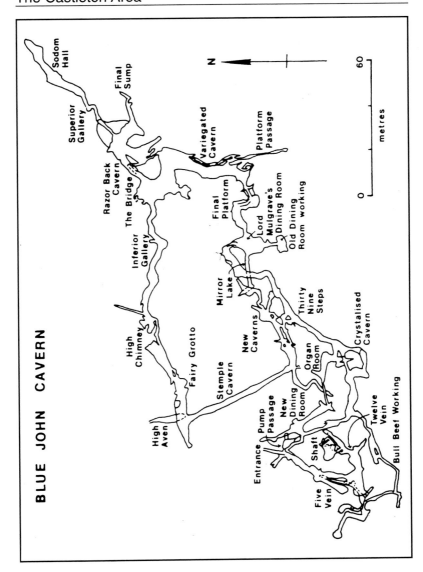

Figure 40. Sketch plan of the Blue John Cavern: the tourist route goes from the entrance (centre left) through Lord Mulgrave's Dining Room to the Final Platform.

The Castleton Area

Blue John Caverns start with a tortuous descent of a slot-like pothole with branches into old Blue John fluorspar workings in palaeokarstic caverns (Figure 40). The route leads into a large vadose canyon, abandoned by all but a misfit stream. Beyond the tourist route tributary passages have more Blue John workings, and the cave ends in the vast Variegated Cavern where the passage suddenly contracts to an impenetrable sump.

Among the non-commercialized caves are Windy Knoll Cave developed partly in the Boulder Bed. In the 1870's it yielded a late Pleistocene bone deposit of some 6000 bones. Adjacent is the famous bitumen deposit. Giants Hole is the longest and deepest swallet cave (Figure 41). Inexperienced parties can traverse the first

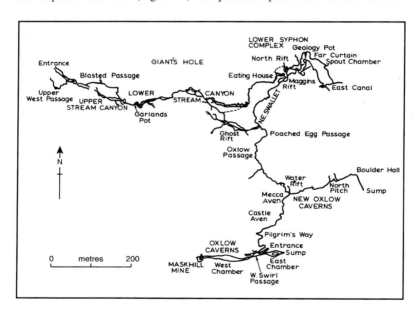

Figure 41. Sketch plan of Giant's Hole and Oxlow Caverns.

section (as far as the vertical drop of Garlands Pot) by wading in the stream (permission from Peakshill Farm). Much of Giants Hole has a classic vadose canyon form up to 20 m high. The system also includes solutionally-widened joint caverns, scattered stalactites and other speleothems, cemented inwashed solifluction deposits, and numerous chert nodules. Beyond Garlands Pot the vadose canyon is a kilometre long but, in places, less than half a metre wide resulting in the name Crabwalk. Using old high level passages a total length of 4 km and depth of some 200 m is mostly accessible **but only to expert cavers.**

The Castleton Area

Figure 42. Eldon Hole: Derbyshire's only open pothole, 60 m deep.

On the southern slope of Eldon Hill is Eldon Hole (Figure 42), Derbyshire's only open pothole, 60 metres deep with a short connecting passage into a large cavern decorated with many stalactites. Ancient legends tell of a connection to stream caverns beneath and modern dye tests have confirmed that the drainage goes to Castleton. However, it is unlikely that the goose alleged to have been thrown down in mediaeval times could have made its way through, with or without its feathers singed by the fires of hell!

Karstic Hydrology

Castleton's underground drainage provides a classic example of karst hydrology, as yet not fully understood. There are two types of input from rainfall; percolation and allogenic. Percolation water is that which falls on the limestone and sinks into the ground. There is virtually no run-off and evaporation is low. Much of the percolation water meets one or other of the impervious volcanic horizons and runs down dip on these until a major joint, fault or mineral vein

The Castleton Area

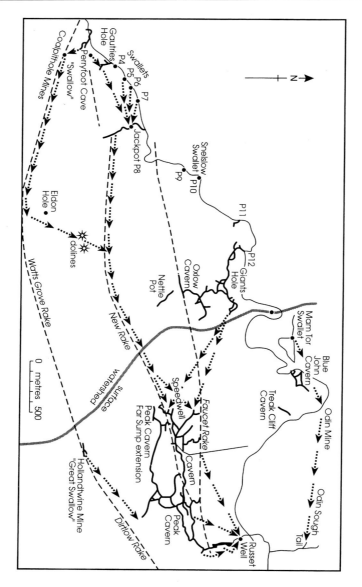

Figure 43. Sketch map to show the hydrological connections (arrowed) between swallets, Speedwell Cavern and Russet Well established by dye tests (modified after a diagram by J.Gunn).

The Castleton Area

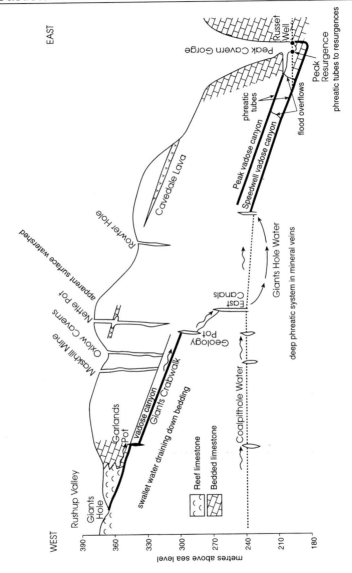

Figure 44. Diagrammatic section to show the underground drainage via swallet caves into phreatic vein cavities, and thence to the streamways of Speedwell and Peak Caverns, with resurgences at Russet Well and outside Peak Cavern.

allows it to pass into lower limestones where it enters the major cave systems as inlet streams and showers. Much of the percolation water gathers to yield the stream in Peak Cavern and resurges into the open just outside Peak Cavern's entrance.

Allogenic water is derived from the rain which falls on the Millstone Grit rocks of Rushup Edge and in the Rushup Valley. The run-off gathers as streams and enters the limestone at or near the limestone/shale contact as a series of swallets (Figure 43). Some of these can be followed for a considerable distance underground, e.g. Giants Hole. In general the swallet streams follow the bedding, but in the reef belt adjacent to Rushup Valley this relationship is less precise. Sooner or later the swallet streams meet a mineral vein and go into the phreatic zone in a sort of U-tube system a kilometre or more in length. The water rises again in one or both of two points in Speedwell Cavern, and flows down that cavern's stream passage for nearly 2 km. It then goes into the phreatic zone and passes under the Peak Cavern gorge to rise at Russet Well (Figure 44).

The main drainage of the area is thus via Speedwell Cavern to Russet Well. Dye tests have confirmed many details and have shown that percolation water from the west of the Castleton area, i.e. around Eldon Hill, joins the phreatic section of the Giants Hole to Speedwell system. The system is therefore swallet - vadose - phreatic - vadose - phreatic - resurgence.

Under conditions of very heavy rain or snow-melt the cave drainage systems are too constricted to allow all the water to pass through easily and floods back-up in the inner parts of both Peak and Speedwell Caverns. Some of the latter's flood water overflows into the former. The resurging streams in Peak Cavern entrance and at Russet Well can be quite spectacular at times, usually on not more than two or three days a year. Observations of several of the cave streams show that under conditions of moderate to high flow they act with intermittent ebbing and flowing characteristics, which can be explained as due to siphoning.

As with all limestone drainage systems, the Castleton caves can be subject to pollution. Occasional spills of sewage, diesel or other unpleasant substances find their way into the underground streams and can be carried for considerable distances, sometimes as far as the resurgences.

The significance of Castleton's karstic features in relation to other parts of Britain is reviewed in the Geological Conservation Review volume on Karst and Caves of Britain (Waltham *et al.* 1996).

The Castleton Area

ITINERARY I

Odin Mine, Mam Tor, Windy Knoll, Treak Cliff

The purpose of this Itinerary is to gain an overview of the many interesting geological features of the Castleton area. The walking distance is about 6 km and an ascent of about 300 m is involved (Figure 45). Allow 4-6 hours. Cars should be left in the village car park (SK 149830). The Itinerary can be shortened by starting and finishing at Odin Mine (Locality 4; SK 134835). Park at the roadside, not in the turning circle.

Much of the land crossed by this Itinerary is National Trust property. Collecting requires a permit.

Leaving Castleton by the A625 westwards towards Winnats Pass, about 100 metres past the petrol station an inconspicuous footpath (marked with a small yellow sign) leaves the road between the houses on the right, almost opposite the Peak Cavern car park. The path leads to a walk up "The Flats" towards Mam Tor. On leaving the avenue of beech trees it is worth pausing at Locality 1 to view the geological framework of the head of Hope Valley.

Locality 1 (145832). The Flats: immediately after the stile the hills to the left and straight ahead are the steep fore-reef slopes of Asbian limestones in Cowlow, Long Cliff and Treak Cliff. A section is cut through these by the Winnats Pass, of which more later. Ahead and to the right are the sandstone hills of Mam Tor and the Losehill ridge. Mam Tor also has its fine landslip scar. Between Mam Tor and Treak Cliff lies the unconformity where the Millstone Grit Series rests on eroded Asbian fore-reef limestones, here cut by the Odin mineral vein.

At various points close to Locality 1 a look down into the stream gully of Odin Sitch reveals the lowest Namurian unit, the Edale Shales, covered to some extent by solifluction deposits and by mine-waste washed down from Odin Mine.

Continue and cross the farm road leading to Dunscar Farm- bear left and follow the stream towards Mam Tor - do not take the marked path past the farm to Hollins Cross on the Losehill Ridge. A tree-covered mound by the farm is one of the spoil heaps from the excavation of the mine drainage level, Odin Sough, in 1816-1822.

Locality 2. Near Dunscar Farm: where the path crosses the stream the channel banks expose much fine- to medium-grained waste from lead ore processing at Odin Mine. In the last two centuries storm run-off has spread tailings widely over the fields, creating "belland pastures" where ingestion of galena and fluorite

The Castleton Area

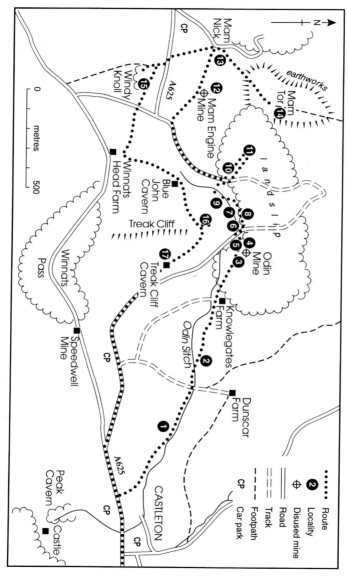

Figure 45. Route map for Itinerary I.

The Castleton Area

particles by grazing animals is a health hazard, particularly to breeding stock. Passing to the left of Knowlegates Farm (138834), the path suddenly climbs steeply on to the bracken and hawthorn-covered toe of the landslipped mass below Mam Tor. A shaft-hollow and spoil mound on one of the shafts on the early 18th century Knowlegates Sough lie on the left. Continue up to the Odin Mine waste heaps.

Locality 3 (135835). Odin Mine waste heaps: close to the path is the fenced-off Knowlegates shaft to Odin Mine. Originally 76 m deep it is now blocked and flooded a few metres down. It was sunk through landslipped material and Edale Shales to about 35 m before reaching limestone, demonstrating that the fore-reef slope clearly visible barely 100 m away on Treak Cliff continues downwards steeply in the sub-surface.

Locality 4 (135835). Odin Crusher: the path crosses the brook where mine waste is abundant, mainly baryte, and a few metres ahead is the Odin Crusher wheel and track (Figure 46). Erected in 1823 for £38-10s-6d (£38.55) the large Millstone Grit wheel with its iron tyre was pulled by horses round a circular iron track to crush the ore from the mine preparatory to buddling (washing through settling tanks) to extract the lead ore. The main road beyond once had a tunnel beneath leading to the mine entrance, but this is now concealed by the turning circle's embankment. Continue up the path to the turning circle at the road end.

Figure 46. Odins Mine's lead ore crushing circle and wheel, erected in 1823 at a cost of £38.10s.6d.

The Castleton Area

Locality 5 (134835). Odin Turning Circle: the circle was built over the southern edge of the Mam Tor landslip and according to the state of repair one or more mini-fault-scarps in the tarmac and grass verge show that the slipped material is still moving! A few metres up the abandoned road near the gate, tear-faulting crosses the tarmac.

Locality 6 (134835). Odin Mine: cross the stile on to the flat grassy area, which resulted from tailings from a 1940's spar washing plant filling in a 6 m deep hollow, burying the original entrance to Odin Mine. On the left the foot of the limestone slope will repay careful examination. It is partly a series of boulders, mainly crinoidal limestone, in a dark, rather shaly limestone matrix - the pre-Namurian boulder bed, which rests on coarse crinoidal fore-reef limestones here. The matrix between the boulders has many derived crinoid fragments and some voids between boulders are filled with blue fluorite. Proceed into the narrow gorge ahead and climb the wedged boulders into the gorge proper.

Locality 7 (134835). Odin Gorge: the walls of Odin gorge show more or less horizontal slickensides demonstrating the wrench fault character of displacement, though a look up to the top of the gorge shows that the shales are some 3 m lower on the south so some vertical displacement is also present. Also, since the mineral vein once filled a 2 m wide gap, there must have been a lateral tensional phase after the initial wrenching. Traces of galena and fluorite still line the walls. The marks of miners' picks are visible in places and sockets for stemples (wooden beams across the vein) are also visible.

Odin Mine was worked from at least the 13th century, possibly as far back as Anglo-Saxon days. It closed in 1869. Workings extend westwards under the southern slopes of Mam Tor for some 1500 metres, and reach to a depth of about 70 m below the portal (just below road level). Plans from the late 18th century show that the mine followed a series of *en-echelon* fractures with linking fractures (Figure 23). A short section of workings is still accessible to those properly equipped and experienced (Figure 21).

Locality 8 (134835). Odin Branch vein: north of the narrow entrance to Odin gorge a small branch vein has peculiar white deposits of the amorphous clay allophane, accessible only by wading. A climb above this branch working takes one across the limestone/shale boundary and up a shale slope. At the top, cross the small grassy ridge to where one can look down into a gully containing Odin Sitch. Beyond the Sitch there are good views of mud-flows on the Mam Tor landslide, but more interesting is the most northerly outcrop of limestone low down near the stream. The relationships to the surrounding shale suggest that it may be the top of a buried hillock on the fore-reef slope. The shales are well exposed in the brook. Continue westwards uphill along the near side of the

The Castleton Area

brook: its channel here is partly an artifical diversion, a leat, made by 18th century miners to keep the stream out of their workings. Dips in the shale are variable as it compacted to the form of the underlying eroded limestone surface.

Locality 9 (133833). Odin Gully: where the brook (in its diversion leat) meets the top of Odin gully it is worth examining the limestone in detail. In the gully proper there are outward-dipping fossiliferous reef limestones with many brachiopods. A few metres up the nearly vertical crag there is a local unconformity where coarse fore-reef limestone with many brachiopod fragments rests on finer-grained reef limestone: mini-potholes can be found along the unconformity. Ramifying algal "tufa" layers are present within the reef limestone above the local unconformity. The reef limestone in the gully here appears to be the lower reef-wall noted by Wolfenden (1958).

Returning a few metres back to the stream, large boulders of poorly layered reef limestone, one with a near vertical dip, project from the Edale Shales and represent the pre-Namurian Boulder Bed. Upstream, near the Blue John Cavern, nearly horizontal back-reef limestones form small crags. Climb up the steep bank on the right to rejoin the road and walk down to the gate.

As an alternative to climbing along the steep shale slopes by Odin gully, omit Localities 8 and 9 and return to the road and walk up round the Hairpin Bend observing the numerous collapses and distortions of the road. Close to the Hairpin Bend a fault scarp 2 m high marks the northern edge of the landslipped mass.

Locality 10 (132833). Mam Tor Turning Circle: the effects of landslipping on the old A625 road are obvious from the viewpoint at the fenced-off road end near the Blue John Cavern track (Figures 30 & 65). Movement tore half the road away in 1976 after repeated fillings of tarmac to level the road failed. It has left an interesting stratigraphy of tarmac and gravel layers with mini-unconformities! One-way light traffic with lights was allowed in 1977 before it became obvious that the road could not be maintained across such unstable ground. To the north of the gate a view may be had towards the main scar of the original Mam Tor landslip which forms a cliff some 130 metres high. Walk across the uneven ground towards the slope at the foot of the cliff face, but do not go close up to the cliff foot owing to the danger of falling rocks, particularly after rain or frost.

Locality 11 (130835). Foot of Mam Tor Landslip Scar: the debris slope below Mam Tor's face provides numerous examples of sedimentary structures in the Mam Tor Sandstones. Of distal deltaic-turbidite facies they include sole markings such as scratch and groove marks where just-suspended objects dragged across the preceding sediment, as well as flute casts, load casts, flame structures and occasional trails. The sandstones themselves have derived shale slabs scattered through them, occasionally in shale-pellet conglomerate layers. Fragments of Carboniferous vegetation are common, even occasional tree branches or stigmarian roots. Mica flakes sparkle on bedding planes, indicating derivation from a micaceous terrain, probably the Dalradian schists of the Scottish Highlands. To the left the flanking cliff is of Edale Shales, too high to be stratigraphically in place beneath the sandstones, so that a concealed fault along the foot of Mam Tor can be inferred, with a downthrow to the northwest. Within the sandstone-shale sequence there are scattered ironstone (siderite) nodules up to 2 m wide and 0.5 m thick. Some show cone-in-cone structures due to recrystallisation under pressure, whilst others have rare solid goniatite fossils. On a terrace some beds of shale contain crushed goniatites and bivalves such as the pectinoid *Dunbarella*. Palaeontological studies have shown that the Edale Shales range from Pendleian to early Kinderscoutian in age (E_1 to early R_1), whilst the whole of the Mam Tor Sandstone was deposited in a short part of R_1 times.

Locality 12 (127833). Mam Engine Mine: return to the road and proceed uphill for some 400 m almost to the road junction where a signed path on the right leads up to Mam Nick and thence to the summit of Mam Tor. The path crosses the remains of the waste heaps from Mam Engine mine. This was sunk through the shale cover to meet the limestone and the Odin vein some 70 m down. The "Engine" was in fact a horse-driven winding "gin" used to raise ore to the surface, where it was crushed and washed. Most of the waste is calcite. The washing was done by gathering water off the hillside above through a system of channels or leats and traces of these can be seen just above the waste heaps. The waste was re-processed early in the 20th century to recover fluorspar for fluxing in the steel industry. Continue to Mam Nick.

Locality 13 (125834). Mam Nick is where the secondary road goes over into Edale. To the west is the hogback ridge of Rushup Edge, the catchment area for the streams draining into the swallets at the limestone's edge. Mam Nick has roadside exposures in the alternating sandstones and shales of the Mam Tor Sandstones. There is a small fault with a throw of 2 m down to the south. A few metres walk towards Edale leads to the first gate on the left where there is a good view across the broken ground of the Mam Nick major landslip.

Locality 14 (128836). Mam Tor: return into Mam Nick and take the slabbed and stepped footpath to the summit of Mam Tor. The summit area is bounded by the ramparts of a Bronze - Early Iron Age fort, and there are traces of hut circles on this bleak defensive retreat. At 517 m O.D. it is the highest point in the Castleton area. The views all round give an opportunity to appreciate the many aspects of the geology. To the north lies Edale valley, floored by Edale Shales in a gentle

The Castleton Area

anticlinal arrangement. An abortive oil-well drilled in 1938 near the railway viaduct at Barber Booth penetrated over 100 m of shales before reaching limestone. The spring line and the change from gentle slopes to steep at about the 1000 ft (c. 300 m) contour mark the top of the Edale Shales and the base of the overlying Mam Tor Sandstones. Above are the proximal deltaic turbidites of the Shale Grit followed by the Grindslow Shales. The massive deltaic Kinderscout Grit forms the plateau. Other small landslip features are to be seen on the north face of Rushup Edge and around much of Edale.

Looking southwest from Mam Tor the view is along the Rushup Valley where streams draining off Rushup Edge are incised into the solifluction sheet mantling the lower slopes of Rushup Edge. The streams plunge into swallet caves on reaching the limestone. One stream has washed solifluction detritus into the upper passages of Giants Hole, which is the longest and deepest swallet cave (Figure 41). The underground drainage passes eastwards beneath the apparent surface watershed to resurge at Russet Well in Castleton (Figure 43).

The limestones along the shale/limestone contact include a series of lenticular reef masses, with fore-reef limestones dipping northwards. A sharply defined small valley separates Middle Hill with reef and fore-reef limestones on the left (south) side from the isolated Peaks Hill on the north. Peaks Hill appears to be a knoll-reef which has flanking beds showing quaquaversal dips (outward dips in all directions). It is almost surrounded by shales and stands out a little way from the general line of the limestone/shale contact. The entrance to Giants Hole is in a short, partly dry valley between Middle Hill and Peaks Hill.

South of this reef belt the massive back-reef to lagoonal facies is largely of Asbian age, well exposed in Eldon Hill quarry. The quarry cuts into Eldon Hill, the highest point on the Peak District's limestone outcrop at about 1500 feet (450 m) O.D. At an earlier stage (early Pleistocene?) the shale and sandstone cover must have extended higher on to the limestone, and there are remnants of ancient swallet caves filled with sediment in Eldon Hill quarry (not accessible to the public).

To the south and southeast the view from Mam Tor covers much of the ground of other excursions in this guide. Due south is Windy Knoll, a high point on the ridge forming the surface watershed. The little quarry at Windy Knoll has unique bitumen deposits. Beyond and to the left is the Winnats Pass, the deep gorge cut through the reef belt. Between the Winnats and the foot of Mam Tor is Treak Cliff, a complex of reef and fore-reef limestones and home to the famous Blue John fluorite deposits, as well as two of Castleton's show caves, Blue John Cavern and Treak Cliff Cavern. The view southeast is across Treak Cliff along the strike of the reef complex to Castleton's Peveril Castle and Peak Cavern

The Castleton Area

Figure 47. View from Mam Tor along Castleton's reef belt: Treak Cliff in the foreground; Peak Cavern gorge and Cave Dale in the centre.

gorge. Beyond, the Asbian reef belt terminates near the Cement Works (Figure 47).

Descend Mam Tor by the footpath back to Mam Nick and take the path on the left down to Windy Knoll. This path and its continuation past Windy Knoll are part of the Portway, an ancient track dating back at least to Bronze Age times. By the wood on the right are more waste heaps from the Forest and Castleton shafts into Odin Mine some 200 m below. The car park there is built on the mine waste heaps from the Forest Shaft.

Locality 15 (127830). Windy Knoll: cross the road and climb the stile. A shaft-mound with hollow top immediately on the right (west) marks a former mine-working on a branch out of Odin Rake. A few metres ahead a buried oil pipeline across the Pennines crosses the path and is marked by an isolated stile. Straight ahead is the old Windy Knoll quarry.

Windy Knoll quarry has several features of great interest. The limestones are Asbian reef complex sediments with scattered fossil corals, brachiopods and a goniatite or two, though mineralized joint faces make these difficult to see. The

The Castleton Area

Figure 48. Windy Knoll quarry and cave. The Boulder Bed forms the roof of the cave, the slope behind and the top of the quarry face.

reef here is the most northerly of the Rushup Valley reef belt and it continues beneath the Edale Shales at the foot of Mam Tor. Bedding is nearly horizontal. Resting on the limestone is the pre-Namurian Boulder Bed which forms the roof of the cavern and the slope above (Figure 48). Prominent fissures in the cliff face have angular boulders of light grey limestone in a matrix of dark muddy limestone and were once described as "Neptunean Dykes", regarded as evidence of a contemporary beach (Figure 9). The fissures are today regarded as fossil grykes of terrestrial origin, part of a palaeokarst. The nearby Windy Knoll Cave yielded thousands of bones of Late Pleistocene mammals such as wild ox, various deer and hyena to Professor Boyd Dawkins in the 1870's. He drew a vivid word-picture of migrating herds with animals falling into a pit-fall trap. This was not in the cave visible today but lay beneath the patch of nettles immediately outside the entrance. Unfortunately the "dig" was back-filled after the excavation and nothing can be seen of the bone deposits today. Collections are in Manchester and Buxton Museums.

Windy Knoll is best known for its unique bitumen deposits. Once known collectively as elaterite, there are about thirty varieties of hydrocarbons recorded now (Figure 18). The most obvious ooze from the scree-like Boulder Bed high on the quarry face (Figure 19). Sticky, yellowish-brown paraffinite encloses rod-like masses of olefinite. Hard black carbonite occurs within a patch of coarse white calcite crystals near the western limit of the quarry. The latter form of bitumen also occurs in hollow fossils through much of the Castleton area. Reddish rubbery mutabilite is present in patches. **No collecting is allowed without written permission from the National Trust.**

From Windy Knoll take the footpath eastwards across the main road towards Winnats Head Farm and thence bear left and follow the track past the Blue John Cavern (see Itinerary III) towards the north end of Treak Cliff. The few limestone outcrops along this walk are in back-reef facies and a new reef-belt emerges from beneath the Namurian shales in Odin Gully and the north crags of Treak Cliff. In contrast to the WSW-ENE orientation of the Rushup valley reef-belt, that in Treak Cliff trends almost due south before swinging round to ESE in Long Cliff and Cowlow.

Locality 16 (134833). North Treak Cliff: where the path crosses a stile and enters a steep gully in the face of Treak Cliff a short branch path on the left leads to crags in highly fossiliferous fore-reef limestones with an eastward dip of some 30°. Close examination of the limestone is recommended here, and the scree slope below provides good samples. The fossils include brachiopods (some 50 species recorded), bivalves, gastropods, cephalopods (both straight and coiled nautiloids as well as goniatites), trilobites, ostracods (up to 1 cm long!), bryozoans, rare corals and sponges, and the ubiquitous crinoid debris. Among the most common brachiopod genera are *Dielasma, Productus, Schizophoria, Spirifer, Martinia* and *Pugnax*. Partial fillings of hollow shells have yielded geopetal fabrics, where the once horizontal fills now dip 8° to the east or northeast, showing that the fore-reef face has been oversteepened tectonically by this amount.

A view down the steep hillside looks on to the waste heaps of Odin Mine visited earlier in this itinerary. Near the foot of the slope a distinct round hollow looks like a karstic doline but is in fact a Nazi bomb crater from May 1941!

If time permits it is worth diverting by walking southwards along the crest of the Treak Cliff ridge to get an appreciation of the Carboniferous submarine topography. The crest would have been the contemporary Asbian reef margin with the outward slope being underwater into the basin and the flat top of Treak Cliff part of the lagoon. The highest crags contain masses of the rugose coral *Lithostrotion martini* (134830). Scattered masses of the laminated algal limestone forming the cores of the reefs are present for about 150 m along the ridge. A panoramic view back to Mam Tor will bring home the strong relief in the palaeo-topography of the eroded limestone mass beneath the unconformable cover of Edale Shales and Mam Tor Sandstones.

Return to the footpath at Locality 16 - do not attempt to descend the steep slope

The Castleton Area

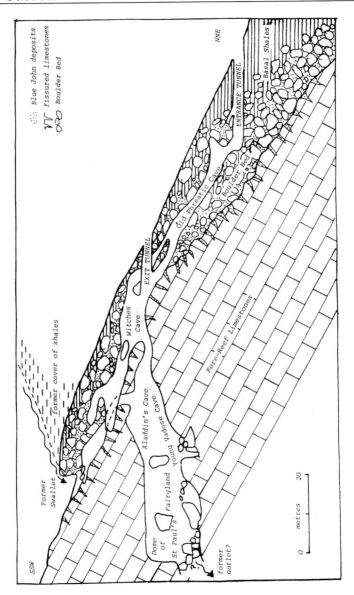

Figure 49. Sketch section of the geological relationships of Treak Cliff Cavern.

owing to loose rocks. Continue down the footpath to Locality 17.

Locality 17 (136832). Treak Cliff Cavern is a combined Blue John mine working and a series of natural caverns (Figures 38 & 49). Though shorter than the other tourist caves it makes up for that in interest. Guided tours depart at frequent intervals. Entry is by a tunnel cut through an outlier of Edale Shales with scattered limestone boulders into the Boulder Bed beneath and it is possible to identify single boulders as much as 6 m wide - effectively blocks of fore-reef which slid down the submerged slope in mid-Carboniferous times. Voids between boulders are sometimes filled with shale or are lined or filled with fine examples of Blue John, some with scalenohedral crystals of calcite in the centre. Much Blue John has been mined here since the mid-18th century. In 1926 miners broke into the inner caverns, a short length of vadose canyon once fed by a swallet on the hillside. It is now a veritable fairyland of stalactites and stalagmites. The discovery of the inner caverns led to the opening of Treak Cliff Cavern as a show cave in 1935. The whole cave system is formed within steeply dipping crinoidal fore-reef limestones or in the overlying Boulder Bed. Yellowish clay on the floors of both series of caverns is derived loess, washed down fissures from the surface. Some of the oldest stalagmites have been dated by U/Th isotope methods at 111,000 years old, showing that at least some of the loessic clay is still older, and that the cavern was high and dry above the water-table by Ipswichian times.

Descend to the old A625 road by Treak Cliff Cavern car park. Edale Shales (partly obscured by scree) are banked up against the fore-reef limestone at the north end of the car park, demonstrating that much of the lower slope of Treak Cliff is a pre-Namurian surface in the process of exhumation.

Walk back to Castleton village down the main road, noting the Winnats Pass on the right, with the adjacent Long Cliff crossed by old lead mine-workings.

ITINERARY II

Cowlow, Speedwell Cavern, Winnats Pass, New Rake, Peak Cavern

The purposes of this Itinerary are threefold: (1) to extend knowledge and appreciation of the Dinantian lagoon-reef basin association; (2) to consider the geomorphology of the Winnats Pass; and (3) to see something of the relationships of Peak and Speedwell Caverns to the surface features.

Walking distance about 4 km, with an ascent of about 250 m (Figure 50).

Park cars in the Castleton village car park (149830).

The Castleton Area

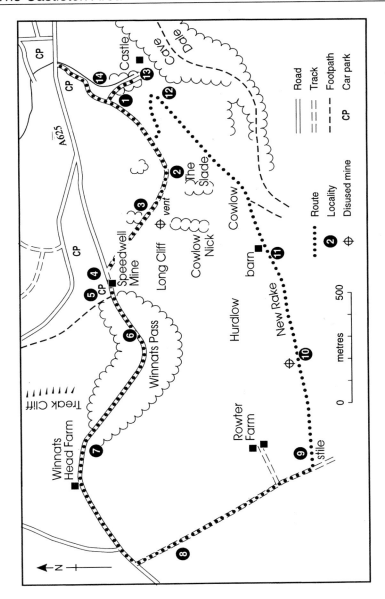

Figure 50. Route map for Itinerary II.

The Castleton Area

Leave the car park by crossing the road and following the brookside path towards Peak Cavern. On crossing Goosehill Bridge, keep straight ahead up Goose Hill until the tarmac ends. Follow the footpath ahead.

Locality 1 (147827). Goosehill Lane: about 20 m after the tarmac ends there are inconspicuous outcrops in the path itself of dark, fine-grained limestones, one of the few appearances of the basin facies in the area and probably equivalent to the Longstone Mudstones of late Brigantian age. In a nearby garden there are underlying coarse crinoidal limestones which may be equivalent either to the lower fore-reef or to the Beach Beds (see below). Continue through the gate ahead and along the foot of Cowlow hillside. The steep slope above the path is almost parallel to the bedding of the fore-reef facies, with dips around 20-30° in shelly detrital limestones.

Locality 2 (144825). Speedwell "Vent": along the foot of Cowlow, when the path makes a distinct bend to the right a low ridge on the left has exposures of the Speedwell "Vent" agglomerate. Other exposures are in the path itself a few metres before the next gate. The agglomerate is a breccia of much-altered basalt blocks up to 10 cm in diameter. Both vesicular and massive basalts are present with a scatter of limestone clasts in an ill-sorted basaltic groundmass. The nature of the "vent" is controversial (Figure 7). The triangular patch of agglomerate is about 200 m long but no contacts with the surrounding limestones are visible. The patch has been interpreted as either the cross-section of a nearly vertical vent pipe at the foot of the fore-reef or as a heap of spill-over debris when the Cave Dale lava spilled out of the lagoon and down the fore-reef through a gap in the reef belt. Traces of glass shards seen in thin section have been taken to support the latter hypothesis. Above the agglomerate outcrop is a short steep dry valley locally known as 'The Slade'.

Proceed through the iron gate.

Locality 3 (143826). Foot of Long Cliff: immediately after the gate a view can be had to the left up Cowlow Nick, the steep gully in the fore-reef, which was probably the beginnings of a dry valley eroded by glacial melt-water. A bed rich in fossil goniatites half-way up once yielded numerous goniatites (Figure 51) including *Beyrichoceras rectangularum* and *Goniatites maximus* but the outcrop has been mostly destroyed by collectors! Numerous 2 mm long juvenile examples of the brachiopod *Dielasma hastata* occur here as well as scattered orthocone nautiloids; fragments can occasionally be found in the scree. Cowlow Nick is also crossed by several scrin veins and the scree contains baryte and a little blue fluorite. The next 200 m along the path after the gate crosses rough ground along the fore-reef slope of Long Cliff. The higher part of the rough ground is grassed-over lead mining waste from Longcliff Vein, which can be

The Castleton Area

traced obliquely up the hillside by the row of shaft mounds. The disturbed ground of the lower slope is due to former quarrying of partly cemented scree for use as road dressing before tarmacadam came into use. Relics of cemented scree can be seen a few metres up the hill slope. These rest on Beach Beds, coarse limestones with water-worn pieces of *Gigantoproductus* valves, best seen in the wall on the right (see discussion under Locality 5 below). An overgrown old Beach Beds quarry in the field below the path was worked for the flat slabs favoured for house building in the village.

Continue along the path to join the road a few metres below the Speedwell Cavern.

Figure 51. Crowded goniatites from Cowlow Nick. A fine-ground slab.

Locality 4 (139828). Speedwell Cavern: guided parties leave every 15-20 minutes. The tour commences with a descent of 105 steps to reach the Main Canal, which is traversed by boat (Figures 35 & 36). The canal tunnel was driven southwards from 1771-1780 through fore-reef limestones into nearly horizontal lagoonal limestone further in. Under Long Cliff the Canal crosses Long Cliff Vein and other small mineral veins to reach the vast Bottomless Pit Cavern after about 500 metres. Rising some 150 metres to the right the cavern has the calcite-rich Faucet Rake vein well displayed, unfortunately with too little

galena to make it worth mining. To the east below the railings is the Bottomless
Pit itself. About 16 m deep to water level and a further 10 m below water, the Pit
swallowed the waste rock from driving the Far Canal tunnel for a further 600 m
beyond the Bottomless Pit. The miners then intersected a series of natural
caverns with a substantial stream flowing from west to east. These caverns had
been reached in the 18th century from mine shafts on the hill-top, so that the
canal tunnel system was designed as an attempt to work several mineral veins
with boat haulage in a fashion comparable to the canal tunnels in the Duke of
Bridgwater's coal mines at Worsley, near Manchester. Somewhat over 2 km of
stream caverns have been explored in Speedwell Cavern (Figure 35), with large
chambers such as Cliff Cavern, Block Hall and Plumptre's Cavern rising 50-100
m above the stream; the last named connects with James Hall's Engine Mine on
New Rake. Exploration of the stream caverns requires wading waist deep and
even swimming a few metres so that the public are not admitted. Details of the
lay-out, geomorphology and hydrology can be obtained from the Speedwell
Cavern guide book and from Ford & Gunn (1992).

Locality 5 (139828) Speedwell Cavern car park upper level: the low quarry face
here is in the Beach Beds. These include numerous fragments up to 10 cm across
of water-worn *Gigantoproductus* shells. The beds can be traced along the foot of
the hill slope towards Treak Cliff Cavern before exposure is lost; they can also

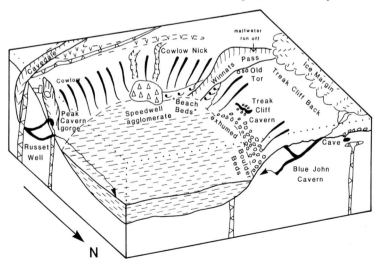

*Figure 52. Block diagram to show the relationships of the Boulder Beds, Beach
Beds and the Winnats Pass.*

The Castleton Area

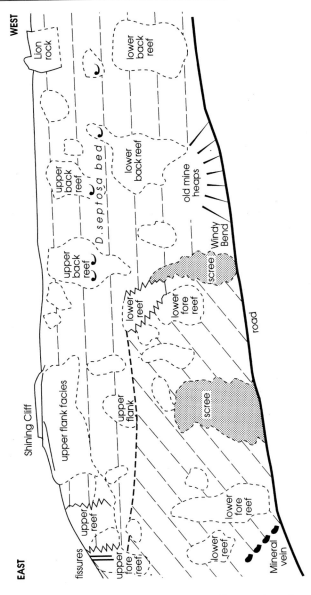

Figure 53. Sketch section along the south side of the Winnats Pass to show the relationships of the Upper and Lower Reef complexes.

be traced southwards back to the foot of Cowlow Nick. Thus, the Beach Beds make a fan-shaped accumulation at the foot of the Winnats Pass and were once thought to represent a fossil beach. A more recent interpretation is that it is a fan

Figure 54. Shining Cliff in the Winnats Pass, composed of flanking facies of the Upper Reef, resting on fore-reef beds of the Lower Reef lower down the slopes.

of material washed down from the lagoon through a proto-Winnats channel coming to rest at the foot of the fore-reef (Figure 52). The abundance of the typically Brigantian brachiopod *Gigantoproductus* shows that the fan is younger than the Asbian fore-reef and may be evidence of the late Brigantian uplift which yielded the pre-Namurian Boulder Bed. Brigantian beds are largely missing from the Castleton area though they appear as a rather cherty series of limestones south of the back-reef high in Cave Dale (see below) and around the Blue Circle cement works quarry, near Bradwell.

Locality 6 (137827). The Winnats Pass: it is worth pausing in near the Windy Bend to work out the stratigraphy of the limestone beds in both walls; the details are rather better seen in the south wall (Figure 53). The outer parts of the Pass show steep outward dips in detrital fore-reef limestones with many crinoid and brachiopod fragments. High on the south side these pass, with grassy gaps between exposures, into the upper algal reef wall (largely hidden by grass) at the

The Castleton Area

eastern end of Shining Cliff (Figure 54). The reef wall is about 15 m high and 10 m long. The main part of Shining Cliff is in beds transitional from back reef to massif facies. In the slopes below Shining Cliff these nearly horizontal beds lie on top of outward-dipping fore-reef beds with the discordance mostly obscured by grassy ledges. The lower algal reef is in the grass-covered lower to middle slopes directly opposite the Windy Bend. A similar situation applies on the higher slopes on the north side of the Pass where the broken nature of the crags obscures the relationship. The lower reef-wall has its top a few metres east of the portal of Old Tor Mine, whilst the upper reef is in the topmost crags about 100 m to the east. The two levels of algal reef-wall with apparent discordance here in the Winnats Pass compare with a similar situation in Cave Dale (Itinerary III, locality 2). A climb from the foot of the Pass halfway up the northern slope to a hollow by a solitary tree reveals an accumulation of shells of the bivalve *Pseudamussium*, some with traces of original colour banding. Beds beneath it have numerous productid brachiopods. Both fossils are characteristic of the fore-reef environment. Keeping to the road and climbing the Pass, a cave on the right is locally known as Suicide Hole: it is short, but unexpected drops make it dangerous to explore without care and good lighting. The road outside lies directly above mine workings and solution caverns in a branch of Speedwell Cavern in Long Cliff Vein some 40 m below the surface; there is no sign of them in the Pass itself. Uphill from the Windy Bend the reef limestone complex passes into gently dipping back-reef to lagoonal beds on the south side, whilst the crags on the north are an oblique section through the Treak Cliff reef complex as noted above. Close to the road on the north, back-reef limestones form low cliffs dipping at about 15° to the southwest. Reef and back-reef beds have local abundant accumulations of fossils, but collecting should be restricted to the scree. High on the north flank a track leads up to the Old Tor Mine (now gated) once worked for Blue John fluorspar. Adjacent limestones are very fossiliferous. A short climb across them leads up to a hollow in the crags also once worked for Blue John fluorspar. Soon after the Windy Bend disturbed hummocky ground close to the road on the south side marks old lead mine workings with baryte-rich waste. Further up an abortive lead mine trial level on the right follows a scrin barely 5 cm wide on the north side of the road.

A diversion may be made before reaching the top of the Pass by climbing the stile on the right and walking up the "Roman Hollow" - a Mediaeval trackway in a short tributary dry valley. This leads on to the top of Treak Cliff where the broken ground is all that remains of former workings for fluorspar which was mined opencast during World War II. A stile on the right leads on to the crest of Treak Cliff, with large colonies of the coral *Lithostrotion martini* (see locality 16 in Itinerary I). Either continue the diversion across the top of Treak Cliff to join Itinerary I near the Blue John Cavern OR turn left over the stile by the farm to rejoin the road at the top of the Winnats Pass.

The Castleton Area

Locality 7 (132828). Winnats Head: at the top of the Winnats Pass an old quarry on the left (south) is in crinoidal calcarenites in the massive facies. Low down is the very tight entrance to Winnats Head Cave. With narrow and unstable entrance passages this is best left to the expert speleologists, but it is worth contemplating that the big cavern within is of cathedral proportions and lies beneath the upper southern slopes of the Winnats Pass with no surface indication of its existence.

From the vantage point of the old Winnats Head Quarry look back down the Pass. It is thought-provoking here to consider the geomorphological history of this gorge (Ford, 1987). It is a short steep dry valley cutting through the reef belt and must have had a powerful stream in it once, but where is the catchment? Barely 1 km^2 of nearly level ground extends up to Windy Knoll and beyond that watershed there is a gentle slope westwards into the Rushup Valley. It is thought that a combination of factors has led to the formation of the Winnats Pass. The stages in its development are thought to be: (1) an inter-reef channel in Brigantian times; (2) further deepening in pre-Namurian times and subsequent filling with Namurian shales; (3) more deepening during run-off in early Pleistocene glacial periods before the Rushup Valley had been incised; (4) late Pleistocene melt-water run-off from an ice sheet when its margin was near Windy Knoll and the ground was frozen; (5) periglacial trimming to the present form in Ipswichian to Holocene times.

Locality 8 (128825). Rowter Farm lane: for the continuation of itinerary II continue up the road past the farm and join the main road. A few metres further on turn left (south) through the gate on to Rowter Farm lane, part of the ancient Portway prehistoric track system. After about 200 m pause at Locality 8 where the track crosses an E-W line of mounds and hollows in the fields on both sides (Figure 55): these mark the western continuation of Faucet Rake, the mineral vein seen in the Bottomless Pit cavern, here known as Horsestones Rake. Some 50 metres to the west a deep hollow probably marks a collapse into a solution cavern like the Bottomless Pit. The Rake continues westwards and about 500 m away, south of Oxlow House farm, is the inconspicuous mine shaft entrance to the vast Oxlow Caverns, another series of solution caverns on Horsestones Rake. From Locality 8 a look back towards Mam Tor will emphasize the relationship of the limestone country to the unconformable cover of the Millstone Grit Series. The former extent of the Mam Tor Sandstones over the limestone can easily be visualized.

Locality 9 (131819). New Rake: continue along the track passing the entrance to Rowter Farm until a high stile is reached on the left. Climb this and take the path eastwards along the disturbed ground marking the former lead mine workings of New Rake towards the isolated barn (Figure 55). Several large hollows mark the

The Castleton Area

Figure 55. Oblique aerial view of the area around Rowter Farm. The line of workings on the left mark the course of Faucet Rake, whilst those to the right mark New Rake (photo by D.Riley).

probable sites of collapses into mineral vein solution caverns.

Locality 10 (136820). New Rake: beyond the barn a stile lies almost over the most westerly point reached by explorers in Speedwell Cavern, here 180 m below the surface. Here, at Main Rising the drainage from all the Rushup Valley swallets wells up from a solution cavity in a branch vein off New Rake. The underground stream flows eastwards down a vadose canyon type of passage some 10 m high. Short tributary streams enter on both sides, one from the vast Cliff Cavern, more than 50 m high, which lies beneath the next stile. Close to the second stile 18th century lead miners sank James Hall's Over Engine Mine shaft and found a way down into the large Plumptre's Cavern and thence into the Speedwell's stream caves. Walking along the grassed-over waste heaps from near-surface workings in New Rake and the closely parallel Horsepits Rake, gives little indication of the subterranean marvels beneath ones feet.

Locality 11 (141822). Hurdlow Barn: the ruined barn is further east along New Rake. The low hill on the left is Hurdlow and small exposures reveal that the summit has an outlier of rather cherty Monsal Dale limestones. From near

The Castleton Area

Hurdlow Barn one can look down to the right into the upper part of Cave Dale, a typical dry valley. Once again the surface gives little clue to the extensive system of vadose stream canyon passages in the inner parts of Speedwell and Peak Caverns which lie beneath this area. The inner end of the latter is submerged, but cave divers have been able to reach large caverns beyond. These lie beneath the triangular field south of New Rake, which shows little evidence of lead miners activities. But, surprisingly, these caverns had been entered by the old lead miners by an as yet unknown route. Part of these "lost" caverns comes close to branches to Speedwell Cavern and a hidden connection is suspected. Continue along the path towards the ruined Peveril Castle.

Locality 12 (147834). Near Peveril Castle, once approached by a drawbridge over the top of Peak Cavern gorge, the path turns north down the fore-reef slope of Cowlow. Before going down one can get good views into the lower parts of Cave Dale, with its section through the reef complex (see Itinerary III). But, to conclude this excursion turn left and descend the fore-reef slope to rejoin the path used at the start of this Itinerary. Then turn right towards the village. On reaching the houses on Goose Hill turn right again and take the path to Peak Cavern. Soon after the last house on the left, just below the path, is Slop Moll where an overflow spring from the Speedwell Cavern to Russet Well drainage rises in wet weather. A small mineral vein crosses the gorge close by and the open gash where is has been worked is visible on the east cliff.

Locality 13 (148826). Peak Cavern: the cavern's huge entrance lies at the back of a short narrow gorge cut through the reef belt. Low down to the left is the resurgence of Peak Cavern's stream. Above this, on the left of the entrance, study the bedding planes which show that the limestones here accumulated as a heap of lenticular shoals to form the foundations of the reef belt.

Tours through Peak Cavern leave every 15 to 30 minutes. Inside the entrance arch is a series of terraces once used by rope-makers (Figure 31). These are cut into late Pleistocene sediments, including much frost scree. Though they are a promising site for late Pleistocene archaeological relics and mammals, they have not been excavated so far. At the back of the Vestibule the passage lowers to Lumbago Walk, sometimes submerged by flood waters in winter. The tour then reaches the Great Cave, which lies beneath Cave Dale, again with little surface evidence for its presence. The cave tour continues towards the Halfway House and Five Arches, before becoming suitable for explorers only (Figure 32). The route to the inner caverns involves passing the Mucky Ducks where water almost meets the roof. Beyond is a magnificent series of vadose canyon passages with several tributaries and a climb to the high level White River Series of "fossil" vadose passages with abundant stalactites.

The Castleton Area

Locality 14 (148828). Russet Well: return to daylight and take the path back towards the car park. Where it reaches the river bank, just short of Goose Hill bridge, look back upstream and a strong flow of water will be seen entering from Russet Well on the opposite bank. This is the drainage from Speedwell Cavern's stream caves, which passes beneath the Peak Cavern stream to resurge on the "wrong" side! It serves to emphasize the complexities of the underground hydrological system (Figure 43). Under flood conditions water backs up in Speedwell and overflows into Peak Cavern. Russet Well may be viewed by prior appointment with Mr Peter Harrison at the adjacent house.

Finally, look back at Peak Cavern gorge, and ask yourself, how did the underground drainage get out in earlier Pleistocene times when the valley floor was perhaps 50 or 100 metres higher than now. It seems that Peak Cavern's entrance and gorge probably acted like a Vauclusian spring, with the water rising from a deeply submerged cave system on to a much higher Hope Valley floor.

Return to the car park.

ITINERARY III

Cave Dale, Dirtlow Rake, Pindale

The purposes of this Itinerary are (1) to examine another section through the Asbian limestones of the marginal reef belt; (2) to see the character of the overlying Brigantian limestones both in Cave Dale and Pindale; (3) to observe the geomorphology of the Cave Dale dry valley; (4) to see the mineralization associated with Dirtlow Rake.

Walking distance about 4 km and ascent of about 200 m (Figure 56).

From Castleton car park walk through the village to the Market Place. At the top (SE) corner the path between the houses leads directly into Cave Dale.

Locality 1 (151827). Cave Dale entrance: the cliffs either side of the narrow entrance to Cave Dale show fore-reef limestones dipping northwards at about 25° (Figure 57). A few metres ahead the small old quarry on the left has similar limestones with primary porosity in the form of *Stromatactis* cavities. Bedding is irregular and often bounds lenticular masses of shelly or crinoidal fore-reef detritus. The beds in the quarry are cut by two small E-W mineral veins. The shallow cave on the right appears to have been developed along a local discontinuity (unconformity) in the fore-reef limestones.

The Castleton Area

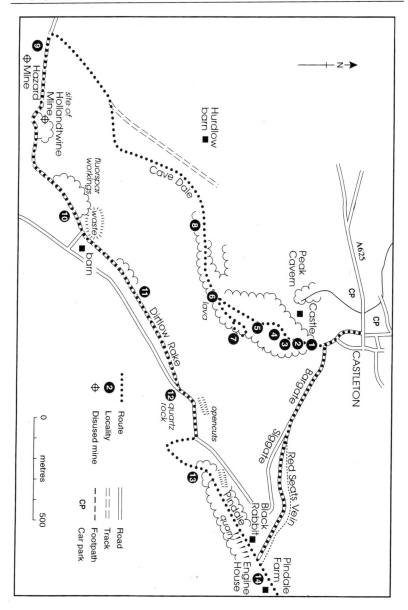

Figure 56. Route map for Itinerary III.

The Castleton Area

Locality 2 (150825). Cave Dale: about 100 m up the dale a low cliff on the left (east) shows a minor unconformity within the fore-reef limestones where one lens of fore-reef detritus channels into another (Figure 57).

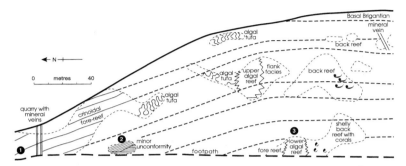

Figure 57. Sketch section of the facies relationships through the reef complex on the southeastern slopes of Cave Dale (modified from an unpublished diagram by Martin Lee).

Locality 3 (149825). Cave Dale: further on as the path up Cave Dale levels out and bends to the right, it is worth pausing to study the stratigraphy and facies relationships of the limestones on the south side (Figure 57). The prominent crag low down on the left is in a nearly horizontal fossiliferous reef build-up, about 9 m high. Thin-sections reveal much fine grained micritic mud, though some show algal lamination and scattered bryozoans such as *Fenestella* and *Penniretepora*. These are thought to help as sediment traps during reef growth. Fore-reef detrital limestone occurs to the left of this crag; to the right is a flanking back-reef facies. Small fossil brachiopods such as *Pugnax* and *Spirifer* as well as many productids and colonial rugose corals are common here. Back to the left the upper slopes are in fore-reef limestones with outward dips around 20-25°. Patches of algal "tufa" (recrystallized algal micrite) are locally common. The fore-reef limestones contain numerous fossils, mainly brachiopods, with productids particularly common. Corals such as *Lithostrotion* are scattered through both fore- and back-reef beds. Occasional goniatites include *Beyrichoceras* and *Bollandites.* Examples of algal lamination and of reef tufa indicate the presence of an upper reef-wall comparable with that in the Winnats Pass. High on the right (north) the crags are a section along the strike: directly below Peveril Castle's keep the crags are in a poorly fossiliferous, upper reef build-up with crinoidal calcarenites on both flanks (Figure 58). Reef and fore-reef facies interdigitate though they are difficult of access. Reef tufa and geopetal fabrics are present though not easy to find. The next high cliff west of the Castle is in back-reef and has an inaccessible lenticular mass of reef limestone in the middle.

The Castleton Area

Across the Dale, high up on the left (southeast) a patch of thin dark limestones about 6 m thick may represent a former hollow within the back-reef complex: the thin dark beds extend both up and down the dale though they soon die out. Some 20 m of massive reef limestone follow and can be traced almost to the top of the hill, where the lowest Brigantian beds are indicated by the appearance of much silicification (Figure 59). The two masses of reef limestone here in Cave Dale may correlate with the upper and lower reef-walls in the Winnats Pass (Itinerary II, locality 6).

Figure 58. View down the lower part of Cave Dale: the cliffs on the right are those shown on Fig.57.

Locality 4 (149824). Cave Dale: in the widest part of Cave Dale, it is worth pausing to reflect that the dale here lies directly above the Great Cave of Peak Cavern, with less than 20 m of limestone between. A little more deepening during Pleistocene periglacial erosion might have resulted in a very different morphology. Consider also that Peak Cavern gorge lies immediately west of the Castle, with only a narrow ridge separating it from Cave Dale: again, a little more erosion and a very different morphology would have resulted!

Locality 5 (149825). Cave Dale narrows: where Cave Dale steepens and narrows again it is crossed by an attenuated New Rake, here little more than 0.5 m of calcite with a short trial working on the left (east). This vein is directly above Roger Rain's House in Peak Cavern, and a trickle of water coming down the dale sinks here to reappear as a shower in the cave below. The next section of

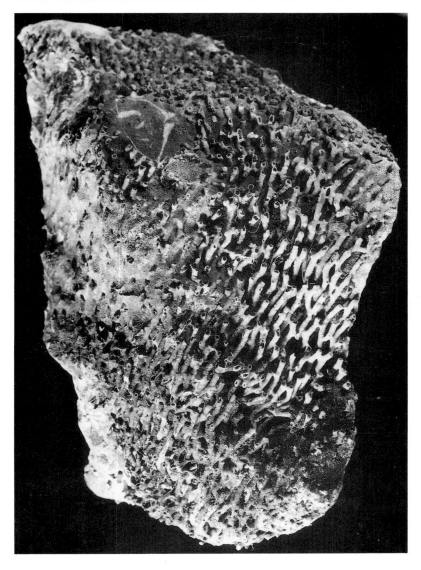

Figure 59. Silicified Lithostrotion junceum *from the basal Brigantian high on the south side of Cave Dale.*

The Castleton Area

dale, rather steeper than before, has crags showing sections through back-reef limestones dipping gently to the southwest. The typically Asbian brachiopod *Davidsonina septosa* can occasionally be found on weathered faces. Climb to the iron gate where there is a distinct slackening of gradient of the thalweg and boggy ground.

Locality 6 (148822). Cave Dale lava: crags of olivine basalt lie on either side of the path within a few metres of the gate. On the left the basalt shows a crude columnar structure spoilt by numerous samples having been drilled out for palaeomagnetism studies. Above, layers of amygdaloidal lava alternating with massive basalt layers suggest that the Cave Dale lava was a multiple flow. The grass bank over the wall to the right (north) shows small crags of massive, vesicular and amygdaloidal basalt totalling about 20 m in thickness, with limestones above. The lava outcrop can be traced for about 200 m up the dale before it disappears beneath overlying limestone beds; it can also be traced along the hillside to the north for perhaps 0.5 km along the crest of Cowlow, where it may have spilled over the reef belt to form the Speedwell "Vent". Underground evidence from mines and caves indicate that the lava thins rapidly westwards. At the base of the prominent crags known as Roger, on the north side of Cave Dale, a deeply weathered ash bed some 30-40 cm thick lies a few metres above the Cave Dale lava. The intervening limestones have several large coral colonies. The Cave Dale lava appears to be on the same horizon as the Lower Millers Dale Lava some 10 km further south, though it was probably erupted from an unknown vent much closer than the Calton Hill vent near Taddington.

Locality 7 (150823). Cave Dale - southern upper slopes: a short diversion from Cave Dale proper is to try to follow the lava outcrop back into the wood to the east and within 50 metres the lava has reduced thickness from about 20 m to zero, presumably dying out where the flows were dammed up by the reef belt though the exposures are insufficient to demonstrate this. A spring here is formed from percolation water draining off the top of the impervious lava. Continue back towards the village along the contour above middle Cave Dale and climb to the first crags. These show massive colonies of *Lithostrotion junceum* and *L. maccoyanum,* typical of back-reef conditions. These upper beds must be equivalent in age to the Millers Dale Limestones further south, but the latters' massive character is not present in Cave Dale. The limestones hereabouts are variable in lithology: some are shelly with numerous *Gigantoproductus;* others are oolitic whilst one band contains nodules of the alga *Girvanella*. This bed is taken as the base of the Brigantian Monsal Dale Limestones though it is not easy to find. Higher up the hillside colonies of *L. junceum* are silicified (Figure 59) and there are many chert nodules in the limestone, a feature often taken as a field guide to the base of the Brigantian. Return to the Cave Dale footpath at Locality 6.

The Castleton Area

Locality 8 (146821). Upper Cave Dale: further up the dale past the Cave Dale lava outcrop the dale takes on a typical dry valley aspect with a gentler gradient (Figure 27). The lower slopes are cut through typical Bee Low Limestones (Upper Asbian) and a few coral colonies may be found. Higher up the dale sides *Girvanella* and chert indicate the onset of the Monsal Dale Limestones. After about 0.5 km pause to reflect on the thalweg: moderate at the bottom, then level, then steep, then moderate again. Opinions vary as to the cause of this: one suggestion is that the steep section represents a rejuvenation head (knick point) resulting from the incision of Hope Valley during the late Pleistocene; another hypothesis refutes this and explains the uneven profile as due to the resistant lithology of the Cave Dale lava having precluded the development of a uniform thalweg.

Figure 60. Swirls in the vadose canyon of Peak Cavern's streamway beneath upper Cave Dale (photo by J.R.Wooldridge).

As upper Cave Dale bends to the left it lies directly above the vadose canyon section of Peak Cavern's streamway (Figures 34 & 60), which then extends

The Castleton Area

under the field to the north towards New Rake and the inner end of Speedwell
Cavern. A few metres ahead adjacent to traces of a mineral vein (Wet Rake),
isolated blocks of the Pindale quartz rock lie just left of the path (the Pindale
quartz rock is discussed later).

Locality 9 (136813). Hazard Mine: continue to the top of Cave Dale and follow
the path up the bank on the left to join the unpaved road on a branch of Dirtlow
Rake near Hazard Mine. Intermittently worked for fluorspar in recent years the
massive vein was mined for lead ore to a depth of nearly 200 m in the mid-19th
century. Beneath the wall on the south is the grass-covered waste hillock of
Packthread Mine. From near the Hazard Mine spar workings one can see that the
vein splits westwards into at least three veins, as shown by the lines of shaft
hollows and mounds across the fields. About 500 m WSW a large waste heap is
by the Portway "Gravel" Pits, not gravel in the usual sense but loose lumps of
ore in yellowish loessic clay. Worked for fluorspar and baryte for the last 20
years or so it is now partly back-filled, but the waste heap contains interesting
samples of baryte as well as quartz replacements of limestone. In the field
between Hazard Mine and the Portway Pits a series of shallow gullies are in
effect miniature dry valleys converging on the vein. They were incised into a
sheet of loessic silt under periglacial frozen ground conditions and cavities in the
vein took the drainage underground. To the south of the spar workings at Hazard
Mine the rising ground is composed of cherty Monsal Dale Beds. The highest
ground about 300 m south of Hazard Mine is covered by heather and peat on a
sheet of insoluble chert residue.

Locality 10 (143814). Dirtlow Rake: the unpaved road trends eastwards more or
less parallel to Dirtlow Rake for the next 1.5 km. A paved road built recently to
skirt future quarry extensions crosses Bradwell Moor to the south. Along Dirtlow
Rake waste heaps yield specimens of fluorspar, generally colourless, as well as
cream or pink baryte, much white calcite and a little galena. Follow the road
eastwards to where it bends round a large open pit. Fluorspar has been worked
opencast here for the last ten years or so. The pit is sited where Dirtlow Rake
crosses an unusual pre-Namurian solution collapse structure (Butcher & Hedges,
1987). What appears to have been a large cavern some 20 m below the
contemporary surface collapsed in pre-Namurian times. With the transgression of
the Edale Shales some of the voids between limestone boulders were filled with
shales, and a later mineralization event led to the other voids being filled with
fluorite, baryte and a little galena. The fissure vein of Dirtlow Rake itself cuts
through this structure with a mineral fill largely of calcite. There is no public
access to the open pit but it may be viewed from the track.

Locality 11 (147817). Dirtlow Rake: continue eastwards down the unpaved road
until the massive waste heap is passed. On the right (south) a line of mounds and

hollows lies obliquely across the new tarmac road into the line of trees and marks the course of a scrin branching out of Dirtlow Rake. In the Cement Works quarry this scrin expands into a complex pipe vein with much fluorspar and baryte. A hundred metres or so past the big waste heap, an alcove on the left allows a few paces walk in to get a view into the opencut where Dirtlow Rake has been cut out to a depth of some 15 m. The walls show horizontal slickensides indicating wrench fault movements on the Rake. (**Danger - do not go into the opencut as the sides are loose!**) Waste heaps along the track side have large blocks of calcite, baryte, some fluorite and occasional galena. It is worth looking at the mineral textures to try to work out the sequence of crystallization events.

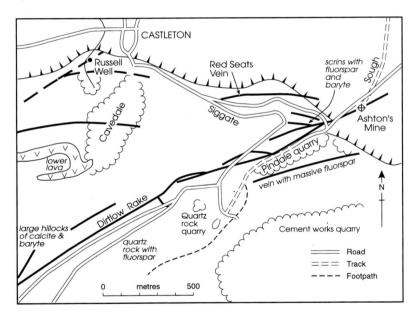

Figure 61. Sketch map of the area around Pindale, showing the quartz rock outcrop and the eastern end of Dirtlow Rake with scrins branching from it.

The limestones on either side of Dirtlow Rake are seen only as scattered low crags. They belong to the Brigantian Monsal Dale Limestones and small outcrops in the fields occasionally yield colonies of the rugose coral *Lonsdaleia duplicata*.

The Castleton Area

Locality 12 (153820). Pindale quartz rock: where the rough road meets the tarmac road the field ahead has large scattered blocks of the Pindale quartz rock (Figures 17 & 61). Others are in the narrow field to the right (south). This unusual rock is a wholesale replacement of Brigantian limestones by authigenic quartz. Thin sections near the margin of the outcrop show a mat of minute doubly terminated quartz needles, with blue fluorite and cream baryte occupying many of the interstices. In the main part of the quartz rock outcrop the quartz crystals show mutually intergrown textures under the microscope. Occasionally the quartz rock encloses chert nodules formed earlier. The origin of the quartz rock is controversial, but it seems likely that mineralizing fluids mobilized silica by the alteration of volcanic ashes and tuffs in the subsurface. A concealed vent lies beneath the floor of the Blue Circle Cement Works quarry and its ferromagnesian minerals are much altered to clay minerals which could have provided the silica.

Across the landscaped area of lead mine waste heaps on the left (north) of the road junction the old open cuts in Dirtlow Rake show quartz rock with blue fluorite in the south wall at one point (Figure 61). Old miners' pick marks are common here too (permission for parties to visit these should be obtained beforehand from the Blue Circle Cement Works, Hope).

Locality 13 (156820). Pindale: continue down the road and turn right by the line of trees and then left down the rough track into Pindale. The first crags on the

Figure 62. Open workings on Dirtlow Rake on the northwest side of Pindale.

right are of quartz rock resting on partly replaced limestone. Further down the long disused Hadfield's Pindale Quarry (158823) shows a section of lower Brigantian back-reef limestones (**danger - much loose rock**). From the track observe that the bedding planes delineate a stack of lenticular accumulations of calcarenite - effectively lime-sand shoals in a back-reef environment. The brachiopod *Gigantoproductus* is fairly common and some beds contain algal nodules with *Girvanella*. The lowest of these is taken as the base of the Brigantian about halfway up Pindale quarry face. Chert nodules are common in the higher beds. The far northeastern end of the quarry (nearest to Hope Valley) has a somewhat brecciated algal reef limestone mass with outward dipping fore-reef limestones beyond. On the left (north) side of the Pindale track the valley side is much broken by mine workings in Dirtlow Rake and several scrins branching from it (Figure 62). Careful mapping shows that Dirtlow Rake is a fault with a downthrow to the south of about 15 m. The buildings at the foot of the dale are all that is left of an old lead miners' settlement known as "Black Rabbit". Directly opposite the single house the tree-covered slope conceals a former exposure of tuff which may represent either the Cave Dale lava or the margin of the vent agglomerate concealed beneath the Cement Works quarry. At the foot of the dale (161824) the limestone/shale boundary is offset by the Dirtlow Rake wrench fault demonstrating a dextral displacement of around 25 m.

Locality 14 (163826). Ashton's Engine House: taking the lane northeast, some 100 m past Pindale Farm, now an outdoor pursuits centre, is Ashton's Engine House, a partly restored lead mine pumping engine house. The mine shaft here passed through some 27 m of Edale Shales and then entered tuff which was not bottomed at 90 m. What had happened to the fore-reef equivalents of the beds in Pindale quarry is not known. A mine drainage sough was driven northwards through the Edale Shales for some 400 m to the Peakshole Water and its course is marked by a line of grassed-over shale mounds in the fields.

Return to the last road junction and either turn westwards along the road back to Castleton or take the footpath just below the road. The latter runs close to Red Seats vein (158826), once noted for its content of smithsonite, the creamy zinc carbonate sometimes called calamine and known to the miners as "dry bone". Road and path both lead westwards back into Castleton's market square.

ITINERARY IV

Losehill, Back Tor, Mam Tor, Blue John Cavern

The purpose of this Itinerary is to look at the lower Namurian beds of the Losehill - Mam Tor ridge.

The Castleton Area

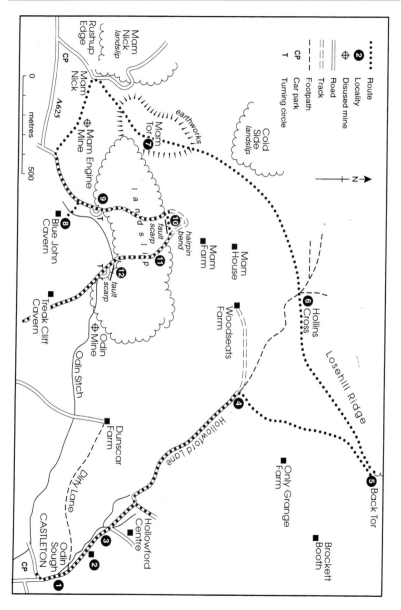

Figure 63. Route map for Itinerary IV.

The Castleton Area

Walking distance about 8 km. Ascent about 400 m. (Figure 63).

Leave Castleton car park by the lower northeastern corner. After a few tens of metres along the lane this joins the Hollowford Road northwards out of the village. Turn left across Trickett Bridge over the Peakshole Water.

Locality 1 (150832). Trickett Bridge: about 10 m after the Bridge a low opening under the stream bank on the left with water issuing is the "tail" or outfall of Odin Sough. This lead miners drainage level was constructed between 1816 and 1822; it is about 1500 metres long and reaches Odin Mine at a depth of 76 m. Almost all of it was excavated through Edale Shales and waste heaps can be found at intervals along the Dirty Lane track which branches off the road a few metres ahead on the left. On reaching the mine the sough was continued along the lowest level of the workings for another 1500 m beneath the south flank of Mam Tor to beneath Mam Nick car park. Most of it is no longer accessible. Continue up Hollowford Lane.

Locality 2 (148834). Hollowford Lane: after about 200 m an isolated building on the right was once the lead miners candlemakers workshop.

Locality 3 (148834). Hollowford Lane: the deep gully on the left has exposures of Edale Shales at intervals, but unfortunately they are unfossiliferous. Take the left fork of Hollowford Lane and continue for about 1 km.

Locality 4 (141842). Foot of Losehill ridge: at a distinct break of slope take the footpath which branches RIGHT (northeast) uphill off the Woodseats Farm road. The break of slope coincides with the stratigraphic top of the Edale Shales and the base of the Mam Tor Sandstones. A glance left and right along the contour shows that there is a line of farms located along this horizon, sited to make use of the spring line at the base of the sandstones. Immediately over the stile take the right hand path up to Back Tor.

Locality 5 (145850). Back Tor (Figure 64): the crag overlooks a landslip scar facing north into Edale and there is much broken uneven ground in the landslipped material below. The scar itself is composed of some 50 m of alternating beds of sandstone up to 1 m thick and rather thinner beds of sandy shale. Collectively they form the unfortunately named Shale Grit, which overlies the Mam Tor Sandstones. The Shale Grit represents a more proximal delta slope turbidite facies than the distal turbidites of Mam Tor itself. Looking across Edale valley the Shale Grit can be seen to form a shelf below the Kinderscout plateau. Several other old landslip scars can be seen too. Turn left (west) along the ridge to Hollins Cross, about 1 km away.

The Castleton Area

Figure 64. The Losehill ridge seen from Castleton, with Back Tor crag on the left.

Locality 6 (136845). Hollins Cross is where the track along the ridge is crossed by an ancient route from Castleton to Edale, with a steep climb up one side and a steep descent down the other! Before there was a church in Edale coffins with bodies were carried this way for funerals at Castleton Church. From Hollins Cross views into Edale show again the break of slope at the foot of the Mam Tor Sandstones and this can be followed round the whole valley head with scattered farms marking the spring line. Detailed mapping shows that the Edale Shales form a very gentle anticline which triggered a search for oil in the buried limestones in the 1930s - to no avail. Beyond Edale village the slopes rise to Kinderscout plateau formed on a massive sheet of delta-top sandstone, the Kinderscout Grit. At Hollins Cross there are scattered sandstone outcrops which show a rather broken and disorganized character with no regular dip. These are taken to mark the presence of a fault which is more or less on a line with one mapped in Edale valley bottom using the numerous exposures of marine bands in the river banks; it also lines up with a small fault visible to the extreme lower right corner of Mam Tor face. Whether these are all one fault is open to debate as no evidence has been found in the intervening ground and both the amount and direction of displacement are variable!

The Castleton Area

Continue westwards along the ridge. As the earthworks are approached, the Cold Side landslip is marked by much broken ground on the slopes overlooking Edale (Figure 28). The steep north-facing hillside gets little sunshine in the winter months - hence its name of Cold Side. Continue to Mam Tor (about 1.5 km).

Locality 7 (128836). Mam Tor summit - see Localities 11 and 12 on Itinerary I.

Descend Mam Tor by the path westwards. There are fine views ahead to the Mam Nick landslip on the northern face of Rushup Edge. Continue down to Mam Nick and take the left hand path downhill past Mam Engine mine's waste heaps to the broken A625 road. Turn left and after about 250 m take the track on the right to the Blue John Cavern.

Locality 8 (132832). Blue John Cavern: this is said to have been discovered by miners about 1770. The Blue John Caverns start with a series of modest-sized stream caverns with branches into shallow-depth workings for Blue John fluorspar. A steep descent down The Pothole, in fact a narrow fissure, leads into a series of impressive vadose stream caverns including the Crystallized Cavern, Lord Mulgrave's Dining Room and the Variegated Cavern (Figure 40). Most of these are dry with only a small misfit stream in the lower chambers. Exploration beyond the tourist route shows that the caverns terminate abruptly at a small sump heading in the direction of Odin Mine, though the water was unexpectedly dye-traced to Russet Well. The route of this concealed drainage may well make use of the void system in the Boulder Bed along the limestone/shale boundary. The presence of this isolated stream cave system so close to the northern limit of the limestone is an enigma as there is so little apparent catchment for a stream big enough to erode these large caverns. Another riddle is that the Blue John deposits of the Blue John Cavern are so close to Odin Rake, but no Blue John is known to have been obtained in the latter. Perhaps Odin Rake and the Blue John pipes represent two different episodes of mineralization.

Return to the A625 road and turn right downhill to the Mam Tor turning circle.

Locality 9 (132835). The Mam Tor landslipped road: pass through the gate at the road end and walk down what is left of the road, last used for traffic in 1979. The landslip is partly block rotation and inwards dips of up to 45° may be seen in sandstones near the road. Movement also involves mud-flow and one such is still active lower down near Odin Sitch. The numerous cracks in the tarmac, sudden changes of road level and disturbed ground all speak for themselves in saying "do not build major highways across landslips" (Figure 65). The distortions in the tarmac effectively simulate the stress, fold and fault patterns illustrated in tectonic text-books. The road was originally built in 1810 as a cart track to serve the lead mines and 20th century road builders simply took over an existing, if unsuitable, route. The road was largely rebuilt in the late 1940's using prisoner of war labour. Corners were cut off and the road re-aligned; parts of the pre-1940's road can still be seen below the remains of the modern road. Much was rebuilt again in 1965 and it was finally abandoned in 1979.

Figure 65. The Mam Tor landslip scar with the disturbed ground below.

Locality 10 (132838). The Hairpin Bend: continuing down the ruined road, the Hairpin Bend is a few metres off the landslip mass, but the road swings south to cross the disturbed ground, which continues as far as Odin Mine (Figure 30). The short cut-the-corner footpath at Locality 10 is along the margin of the landslip and a fault scarp some 2 m high occurs along the edge of the moving ground. The fault scarp is still growing owing to continued movement (see Locality 4 in Itinerary I).

Locality 11 (133838). Below the Hairpin Bend: continuing down the road across the lower part of the landslip, a stretch with considerable disturbance is crossed where part of the road has slipped into the fields below. The remaining tarmac has several small fault scarps.

Locality 12 (134835). Odin Mine turning circle: broken tarmac continues at intervals down to the turning circle by Odin Mine where movement along the right-hand (southern) margin of the landslipped mass causes intermittent disturbance to both turning circle and road. Another small fault scarp can be seen by the miners' crushing circle below the road; this and the fault across the turning circle are in line but they throw in opposite directions demonstrating that a scissor movement is taking place here.

Continue down the road to Castleton.

FURTHER READING

ALLEN, J.R.L. 1960. The Mam Tor Sandstones - a turbidite facies of the
Namurian deltas of Derbyshire. *Journal of Sedimentary Petrology,* **30,** 193-208.
BROADHURST, F.M. & SIMPSON, I.M. 1973. Bathymetry on a Carboniferous
reef. *Lethaia,* **6,** 367-381
BUTCHER, N.J.D. & HEDGES, J.D. 1987. Exploration and extraction of
structurally and lithostratigraphically controlled fluorite deposits in the Castleton-
Bradwell area of the South Pennine Orefield. *Transactions of the Institution of
Mining & Metallurgy,* Section B, Applied Earth Science, **96,** B149-155.
COLLINSON, J.D. 1968. Deltaic sedimentation units in the Upper
Carboniferous of Northern England. *Sedimentology,* **10,** 233-254.
COPE, F.W. 1958, (revised 1965) *The Peak District.* Geologists Association
Guide no.26, 27pp.
DOORNKAMP, J.C. 1990. Landslides in Derbyshire. *East Midland Geographer,*
13, 33-62.
FORD, T.D. 1977. *Limestones and caves of the Peak District.* Geo-Books,
Norwich, 469pp.
FORD, T.D. 1987. The origin of the Winnats Pass, Castleton, Derbyshire.
Mercian Geologist, **10,** (4), 241-249.
FORD, T.D. 1986. The evolution of the Castleton cave systems. *Mercian
Geologist,* **10,** (2), 91-114.
FORD, T.D. 1990. *The Story of the Speedwell Cavern, Castleton.* Published by
The Speedwell Cavern, Castleton. 6th ed. 32pp.
FORD, T.D. 1992. *Treak Cliff Cavern and the Story of Blue John stone.* Harrison
Taylor & Co., Castleton 24pp
FORD, T.D., GASCOYNE, M & BECK, J.S. 1983. Speleothem dates and
Pleistocene chronology in the Peak District of Derbyshire. *Cave Science,* **10,** (2),
103-115.
FORD, T.D. & GUNN, J. 1992. *Caves and Karst of the Peak District.* - an
excursion guide book. British Cave Research Association.
FORD, T.D. & QUIRK, D.G. 1995. Mineralization of the South Pennines.
Geology Today, **11,** (5), 172-177.
FORD, T.D. & RIEUWERTS, J.H. 1976. Odin Mine, Castleton. *Bulletin of the
Peak District Mines Historical Society,* **6,** (4), 54pp.
FORD, T.D. & RIEUWERTS, J.H. 1983. *Lead Mining in the Peak District.* Peak
Park Publication, Bakewell. 3rd ed. 160pp.
FORD, T.D., SARJEANT, W.A.S. & SMITH, M.E. 1993. The Minerals of the
Peak District. *Bulletin of the Peak District Mines Historical Society,* **12,** (1), 16-55.
IXER, R.A. & VAUGHAN, D.J. 1993. *Lead-zinc-fluorite-baryte deposits of the
Pennines, North Wales and the Mendips.* pp.355-418 in "Mineralization in the
British Isles: edited by R.A.D. Pattrick and D.A. Polya, Chapman & Hall,
London. 499pp.

The Castleton Area

NEVES, R & DOWNIE, C. (editors) 1967. *Geological Excursions in the Sheffield Region.* University of Sheffield, 163pp.

ORME, G.R. 1974. Silica in the Viséan limestones of Derbyshire. *Proceedings of the Yorkshire Geological Society,* **40,** 63-104.

PARKINSON, D. 1947. The Lower Carboniferous of the Castleton District, Derbyshire. *Proceedings of the Yorkshire Geological Society,* **27,** 99-125.

PARKINSON, D. 1954. Quantitative studies of Brachiopoda from the Lower Carboniferous of England. *Journal of Palaeontology,* **28,** 367-381, 563-574 & 668-676.

PIGOTT, C.D. 1962. Soils on the Derbyshire limestone: part 1, parent materials. *Journal of Ecology,* **50,** 145-155.

QUIRK, D.G. 1993. Origin of the Peak District orefield. *Bulletin of the Peak District Mines Historical Society,* **12,** (1), 4-15.

SHIRLEY, J. & HORSFIELD, E.L. 1940. The Carboniferous Limestone of the Castleton-Bradwell area, north Derbyshire. *Quarterly Journal of the Geological Society, London,* **96,** 271-299 & **97,** 180-181.

SIMPSON, I.M. 1982. *The Peak District.* Unwin, London. 120pp.

SIMPSON, I.M. & BROADHURST, F.M. 1969. A Boulder Bed at Treak Cliff, north Derbyshire. *Proceedings of the Yorkshire Geological Society,* **37,** (2), 141-152.

SKEMPTON, A.W., LEADBEATER, A.D. & CHANDLER, R.J. 1989. The Mam Tor Landslide, North Derbyshire. *Philosophical Transactions of the Royal Society,* **A329,** 503-547.

STEVENSON, I.P. & GAUNT, G.D. 1971. *The Geology of the Country around Chapel-en-le-Frith.* Memoir of the Geological Survey of Great Britain. 430pp.

WALTERS, S.G. & INESON, P.R. 1981. A review of the distribution and correlation of igneous rocks in Derbyshire, England. *Mercian Geologist,* **8,** (2), 81-132.

WALTHAM, A.C., SIMMS, M.J., FARRANT, A.R. & GOLDIE, H.S. 1996. *Karst and Caves of Great Britain.* Chapman & Hall, London.

WOLFENDEN, E.B. 1958. Paleoecology of the Carboniferous reef complex and shelf limestones in North Derbyshire. *Bulletin of the Geological Society of America,* **69,** 871-898.

ACKNOWLEDGEMENTS

Thanks are due to Professor John Gunn and Dr Martin Lee for permission to use some of their diagrams and to Jerry Wooldridge, F.R.P.S. and Paul Deakin, F.R.P.S. for some of their photographs. Particular thanks are due to Mrs Kate Moore of the Geography Dept. University of Leicester, for drafting most of the numerous diagrams.

GEOLOGISTS' ASSOCIATION GUIDES

The following additional Guides, and current prices, are available from
Geological Society Publishing House, Unit 7, Brassmill Enterprise Centre, Brassmill Lane, Bath, BA1 3JN. Credit card orders are accepted by telephone or fax. Tel: 01225 445046. Fax: 01225 442836.

No 2 The Lake District 1990	No 46 Isle of Man 1993
No 7 Geology of Manchester Area 1991	No 47 Coastal Landforms of West Dorset 1992
No 19 West Cornwall 1994	No 50 Southern Cyprus 1994
No 23 Dorset 1993	No 51 The Island of Bute 1995
No 32 Isle of Arran 1989	No 52 Iceland 1994
No 34 Yorkshire Coast 1992	No 53 Eastern & Central Jamaica 1995
No 42 Mallorca 1990	No 54 Aberystwyth District 1995
No 43 Costa Blanca 1990	No 55 Early Cretaceous Environments of the Weald
No 44 Late Precambrian Geology Scottish Highlands and Islands 1991	